BIZARRE BAROMETERS

and Other Unusual Weather Forecasters

Also by the author and published by Baros Books:

Aneroid Barometers and their Restoration

Barographs

Care and Restoration of Barometers

Also published by Baros Books:

Antique Barometers: an Illustrated Survey by Edwin Banfield

The Banfield Family Collection of Barometers by Edwin Banfield

Barometer Makers and Retailers 1660–1900 by Edwin Banfield

Barometers: Aneroid and Barographs by Edwin Banfield

Barometers: Stick or Cistern Tube by Edwin Banfield

Barometers: Wheel or Banjo by Edwin Banfield

The History of the Barometer by W. E. Knowles Middleton

The Italian Influence on English Barometers by Edwin Banfield

A Treatise on Meteorological Instruments by Negretti & Zambra

BIZARRE BAROMETERS

and Other Unusual Weather Forecasters

Philip R. Collins

Baros Books

© Philip R. Collins 2004
First published 2004

Baros Books
5 Victoria Road
Trowbridge
Wiltshire
BA14 7LH
UK

A CIP catalogue record for this book is available from the British
Library.
ISBN: 0-948382-13-9

Typeset and illustrations scanned by:
Ex Libris Press
1 The Shambles
Bradford on Avon
Wiltshire

Printed and bound in Great Britain by:
Cromwell Press
Trowbridge
Wiltshire

Contents

Preface

This book developed from the talks I have given to coachloads of visitors to Barometer World at Merton in Devon. Discussions would turn from the rare barometer, to the unusual, and then to the downright peculiar! During my research into many types of barometer I have discovered a fascination for those weird and wonderful sorts of weather predictor that have so often popped up in library books or at auction. I hope the reader will share with me some of the light-hearted fun I have had in compiling this book, and perhaps look at weather forecasting in a different light.

Some of the items presented here were serious attempts at weather predicting; others obviously were not! Just which are which I cannot always be certain. I wonder how many other such 'instruments' await re-discovery and just how many have been lost altogether. If you know of any unusual weather instruments or weather predictors that are not within these pages, please contact me at Barometer World, Merton, Devon: my obsession with barometers continues to grow as ever.

Acknowledgements

I am most deeply indebted to W. Keith Hollis of Bermuda for taking up the challenge in 2000 to supply me with 'the real stuff' for my experiments with shark oil barometers. He has become a good 'cyber' friend, and it was his determination, above all else, that spurred me on to write this curious little book. He has been dedicated in providing me with information about shark oil barometers and has never once failed to supply quantities of shark liver oil for testing and experimenting here in the UK. I owe it to him to set down here for interested readers both his experience of shark oil barometers in Bermuda and the results of my own experiments with the shark oil supplied by him.

I am also indebted to Sir Roy Sawyer, the world's authority on medicinal leeches, who helped me greatly with the production of the Tempest Prognosticator and has furnished me with a number of articles regarding leeches.

I am also grateful to all those many helpers who have supplied me with various items or snippets of information which have led me to yet another 'find'. Not least, I am indebted to my ever-patient wife, who even allowed the leeches into our bedroom for overnight observations!

The following societies and individuals have generously allowed me to reproduce illustrations for which I am most grateful:

W. Keith Hollis for Figures 3.3–3.8.

The National Trust for Figure 4.2.

The Royal Meteorological Society for Figures 4.5–4.8.

John Forster for Figures 4.19–4.22, 4.24, 7.19–7.21.

Whitby Literary and Philosophical Society for Figure 5.3.

Every effort has been made to trace all the copyright owners, but if any has been inadvertently overlooked, the publisher will be pleased to make the necessary arrangement at the first opportunity.

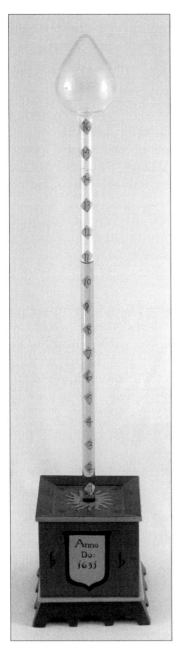 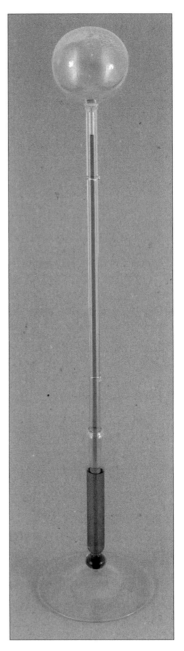

Left, Figure 1.1: Reproduction of an early weather glass by Philip Collins, Merton, Devon.
Right, Figure 1.2: Reproduction of a Santorio thermoscope by Philip Collins, Merton, Devon.

1 Early Weather Glasses

Before the advent of the mercury barometer, invented by Evangelista Torricelli around 1643, there were undoubtedly types of instruments used in Europe which became commonly known as weather glasses. According to the *Oxford English Dictionary*, the earliest written record of the term is by Francis Bacon in 1628. One of the most famous of these early weather glasses, thanks to an illustration surviving in the British Museum, is one that we have reproduced at Merton and is shown in Figure 1.1. The surviving illustration shows how to make the item and where to buy it and is dated 1631.

It is the simplest type of weather glass one can imagine, and almost certainly barometers today that we often hear people calling 'glasses' relate to this type of weather or water glass. It pre-dates the quicksilver weather glass, which later became known more generally as a barometer. The early forms of weather glass were, however, quite crude and, since they trapped air in a bowl, they were very susceptible to temperature. Indeed, the earliest ones were also known as 'thermoscopes' and the effect of pressure variation was probably then unknown.

As weather glasses became instruments for measuring temperature, one must look to books on the history of temperature, and particularly to *A History of the Thermometer and its Uses in Meteorology* by W. E. Knowles Middleton, for an interesting introductory chapter on early thermometers or weather glasses. Knowles Middleton writes of the weather glass, quoting a passage from Robert Fludd's *The Microcosm* (1626) on the weather glass 'commonly known and used among us', as being an old instrument, in another form relating back to probably the earliest known description of a thermoscope-type weather glass of Philo's work from a twelfth- or thirteenth-century manuscript, now in the Bodleian Library (MS Digby 40) (Middleton, 1966: 19).

Weather glasses, as generally described and used in the early seventeenth century, and perhaps in the sixteenth century, tend to be all of a similar type. Figure 1.2 shows a reproduction of one of Santorio's thermoscopes, which, instead of having markings on it, has two threads tied around the stem, presumably to mark the hottest and coldest degrees, although in fact, of course, it is pressure-related as well as sensitive to temperature.

We may perhaps credit Galileo with being the originator of these instruments. Knowles Middleton, in his *History of the Thermometer* (1966: 8), quotes a letter of 20 September 1638 from Castelli to Mgr Ferdinando Cesarini regarding: 'an experiment shown me by our Signor Galileo more than thirty-five years ago. He took a small glass flask, about as large as a small hen's egg, with a neck about two spans long and as fine as a wheat straw, and warmed the flask well in his hands, then turned its mouth upside down into a vessel placed underneath, in which there was a little water. When he took away the heat of his hands from the flask, the water at once began to rise in the neck, and mounted to more than a span above the level of the water in the vessel. The same Sig. Galileo had then made use of this effect in order to construct an instrument for examining the degrees of heat and cold.'

This indicates that this type of weather-glass experiment was known in 1603 and, from accounts during Galileo's early days at Padua, probably between 1592 and 1597. Instruments of glass with water and air for observing changes of heat and cold were known to Galileo. It is probable therefore that weather glasses were certainly around towards the end of the sixteenth century and were considerably more common by the early seventeenth century. It is strange that none of these survives. I have not come across any of these types of weather glass.

Although printed examples are rare, there is an interesting assortment of weather glasses illustrated in *The Mysteries of Nature and Art* by John Bate, first published in 1634. There is also the following description: 'A weather glass is a structure of at the least two glasses, sometimes of three, four or more, as occasion serveth, enclosing a quantity of water, and a portion of air proportionable; by whose condensation or rarefaction the included water is subject unto a continual motion, either upward or downward; by which motion of the water is commonly foreshown the state, change, and alteration of the weather. For, I speak no more than what my own experience has made me bold to affirm; you may (the time of the year, and the following observations understandingly considered) be able certainly to foretell

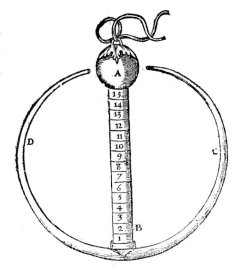

Figure 1.3: Circular weather glass from John Bate's The Mysteries of Nature and Art *(1634).*

the alteration or uncertainty of the weather a good many hours before it come to pass.'

Bate describes several sorts of weather glass and states that there are principally two types: the circular and the perpendicular. It is therefore clear that weather glasses by this period had become quite varied in design and manufacture and must have been quite common. Figure 1.3 shows the circular weather glass: the water will ascend the glass AB in the cold but with heat it will descend in the glass AB, and ascend the horns of the glass CD. It is a most curious and interesting item and one that we have made at Merton in facsimile. It is extremely sensitive to heat as well as pressure. I particularly marvel at the skills of the early glass blowers, who made such instruments using the most rudimentary of lamps to heat and mould the glass.

Of the perpendicular type, there is an interesting selection of styles shown in Figures 1.4 and 1.5. These all appear to be held in a frame structure to support the glass tube or tubes. The illustration shown in Figure 1.6, taken from the frontispiece of the third edition of Bate's book, shows a columned frame supporting the globe above, connected by a glass tube, with a numbered scale on it, to the reservoir below, which is covered to represent the earth or mountains. The effect of covering over the reservoir would, of course, give some temperature stability because of the bulk of material.

But seventeenth-century ingenuity did not end here. Figure 1.7 shows yet another variation on the weather glass where the rising and falling of the liquid alters the weight of the weather glass K and

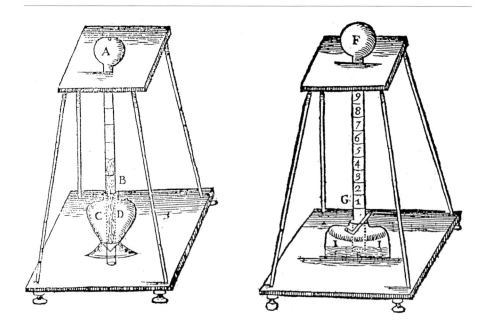

Figure 1.4: Two types of perpendicular weather glass from John Bate's The Mysteries of Nature and Art *(1634)*.

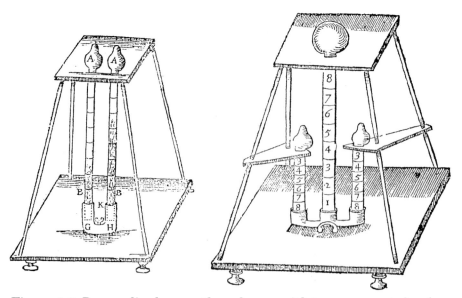

Figure 1.5: Perpendicular weather glasses with two or more tubes from John Bate's The Mysteries of Nature and Art *(1634)*.

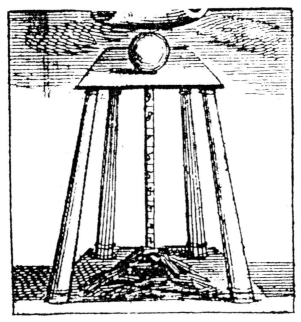

Figure 1.6: Weather glass representing the world from the frontispiece of the third edition of John Bate's The Mysteries of Nature and Art *(1654).*

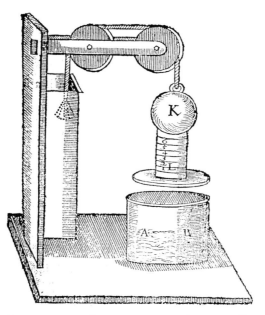

Figure 1.7: Early seventeenth-century moving weather glass.

actually lifts the whole weather glass and water up and down in the reservoir AB through the rope going over the pulley wheels, counterbalanced by lead weights. I can well imagine these curious instruments astounding our seventeenth-century ancestors.

Robert Fludd (1574–1637) was an exceptional scholar who was involved in many scientific areas, including Rosicrucianism and geomancy. He produced many books on a variety of subjects. He associated weather with sickness; in volume II of his work, *The Microcosm*, part IV 'Meteorologia Cosmica', printed in 1626, he illustrates a number of weather glasses in connection with weather and sickness and illustrates an almost identical weather glass to that shown in Figure 1.6: 'you see it depicted here just as you would find it in my house. To make it more wonderful and entertaining, beneath artificial rocks and the tube made of glass and held by an elegant wood framework.'

According to W. E. Knowles Middleton, there is some debate about whether Fludd or Galileo, or indeed Santorio or Drebbel, was the first to invent the thermoscope or weather glass. Certainly it would appear, even by the surviving illustrations and descriptions, that weather glasses were very numerous and no doubt much sought after. Regrettably, there seem to be no surviving models.

Readily available today, though, through numerous outlets, is what is commonly called the 'thunder bottle', or what in America is perhaps better known as the Cape Cod barometer, as shown in Figure 1.8. Often referred to as the oldest type of barometer, although as yet I have not come across any evidence of their early use, they apparently go back many hundreds of years according to 'advertising descriptions'. It is possible that the Pilgrim Fathers had one on board ship, for I have seen an example of one with a saucer moulded in the bottom to contain any spills. It would have been held from a central beam and could have swung from the ceiling of a ship quite safely.

The Victorians continued the use of a simple weather glass (Figure 1.9), which is an oval-shaped bulb with a tube attached upside down in an open-necked bottle or pot; many older readers may perhaps remember making a similar item with a jam jar. This instrument can still be made at home if a suitable bottle with a long neck can be found; it works on exactly the same principle as the early seventeenth-century weather glass.

We have designed our own type of weather glass known as the Collins Patent Table Barometer, which is illustrated in Figure 1.10.

 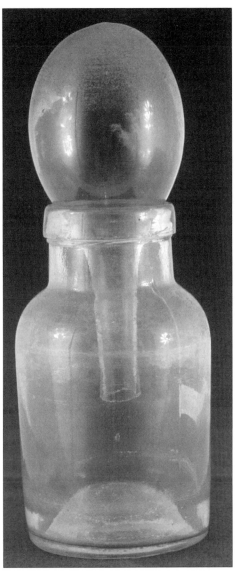

Left, Figure 1.8: A 'thunder bottle'.
Right, Figure 1.9: A Victorian weather glass.

Figure 1.10: The 'Collins Patent Table Barometer'.

It has the advantage of being self-condensing, and therefore requires little topping up, and the spiral expands the movement of the liquid.

2 Storm Glasses

Anyone who becomes interested in barometers will inevitably come across Admiral FitzRoy barometers before too long. Mounted on the domestic version of many of these barometers, as illustrated in Figure 2.1, is often a glass tube with a strange-looking liquid inside it. If it is an old barometer, the liquid may have dried up, with just a few residual crystals left towards the bottom. But just what are these curious phials and what relationship do they have to Admiral FitzRoy, barometers or the weather?

Admiral FitzRoy referred to these glass phials as 'storm bottles'. They are sometimes called 'camphor glasses' or 'weather glasses', but as they are probably best known as 'storm glasses' I will refer to them by this term throughout the book. It has so far been impossible to determine the exact origins of storm glasses. Their discovery may well have been the result of early alchemists noting changes in this peculiar mixture which were thought to be a portent of coming weather. It is perhaps possible to imagine the dark-robed alchemist mixing up potions and discovering, one cold morning in his rooms, that the crystals within the glass bottle had changed. Of course, this would inevitably have preceded some particular weather event, and so such discoveries were linked to foretelling the weather. After all, mercury barometers had not yet been invented.

However, it is perhaps too easy to picture such a romantic notion in order to explain what hitherto has been inexplicable. Admiral FitzRoy, in *The Weather Book* (1863: 443), comments that considerably more than a century ago what were called 'storm glasses' were made in Britain. Who the inventor was is now uncertain but they were sold *'on old London Bridge'* at the sign of the *'Looking Glass'*. FitzRoy's discussion of the storm glass gives his opinion of them, obviously after some research. As it is relatively short, it follows here in its entirety:

> *'Camphor Glass:* Having often noticed peculiar effects on certain instruments used as weatherglasses that did not seem to be caused by pressure, or solely by temperature, by dryness

9

or by moisture – having found that these alterations happened with electric changes in the atmosphere that were not always preceded or accompanied by movement of mercury in a barometer, and that, among other peculiarities, increase or diminution of winds, in the very "heart" of the trades, caused effects on them, while the mercurial column remained unaltered, or showed only the slight inter-tropical diurnal change (as regular there as a clock), we have long felt sure that another agent might be traced.

'Since 1825 we have generally had some of the vials as curiosities rather than otherwise, for nothing certain could be made of their variations until lately, when it was fairly demonstrated that if fixed undisturbed, in free air, not exposed to radiation, fire or sun, but in the ordinary light of a well-ventilated room, or preferably in the outer air, the chemical mixture in a so-called storm glass varies in character with the direction of the wind – not its force, specially, though it may so vary (in appearance only) from another cause, electrical tension.

'As the atmospheric current veers towards, comes from or is only approaching from the polar direction, this chemical mixture – if closely, even microscopically watched – is found to grow like fire, yew or fern leaves – or like hoar frost – or even large but delicate crystallisations.

'As the wind, or great body of air, tends more from the opposite quarter, the lines or spikes – all the regular hard or crisp features, gradually soften and diminish till they vanish.

'Before and in a continued southerly wind the mixture sinks slowly downward in the vial, till it becomes shapeless, like melting white sugar.

'Before or during the continuance of a northerly wind (polar current), the crystallisations are beautiful (if the mixture is correct, the glass a fixture, and duly placed); but the least motion of the liquid disturbs them.

'When the main air currents meet, and turn towards the west, making easterly winds, stars are more or less numerous and the liquid dull, or less clear. When, and while they combine by the west, making westerly wind, the liquid is clear, and the crystallisation well defined, without loose stars.

'While any hard or crisp features are visible below, above or at the top of the liquid (where they form for polar wind) there is plus electricity in the air; a mixture of polar current co-existing in that locality with the opposite or southerly.

'When nothing but soft, melting, sugary substance is seen, the atmospheric current (feeble or strong as it may be) is southerly with minus electricity, unmixed with and uninfluenced by the contrary wind.

'Repeated trials with a delicate galvanometer, applied to measure electric tension in the air, have proved these facts, which are now found useful for aiding, with the barometer and thermometers, in forecasting weather.

'Temperature affects the mixture much, but not solely; as many comparisons of winter with summer changes of temperature have fully demonstrated.

'A confused appearance of the mixture, with flaky spots, or stars, in motion, and less clearness of the liquid, indicates south-easterly wind, probably strong – to a gale.

'Clearness of the liquid, with more or less perfect crystallisations, accompanies a combination, or a contest, of the main currents, by the west, and very remarkable these differences are – the results of these air currents acting on each other from eastward, or entirely from an opposite direction, the west.

'The glass should be wiped clean, now and then, – and two or three times in a year the mixture should be disturbed, by inverting and gently shaking the glass vial.

'The composition is camphor – nitrate of potassium and Sal ammoniac – partly dissolved by alcohol, with water, and some air, in hermetically sealed glass.

'There are many imitations, more or less incorrectly made.

'Those camphor glasses used by the writer lately were prepared by Messrs Negretti and Zambra. There are numerous others, some of which are inexact in chemical composition; and are not nearly so sensitive.'

Admiral FitzRoy is famous for helping to design and place storm barometers of a conventional form around the coast for weather forecasting from barometric readings. It is almost certain that, after his death, firms like Negretti & Zambra produced the type of domestic FitzRoy barometer seen in Figure 2.2, and a few years later the simpler version seen in Figure 2.3, and placed upon them the storm glass.

Left, Figure 2.1: A storm glass mounted on an Admiral FitzRoy barometer restored by Barometer World Ltd, Merton, Devon.
Right, Figure 2.2: Domestic Admiral FitzRoy barometer, circa 1875.

Due to popular interest, and perhaps early marketing skills, it has remained on the majority of these types of barometer ever since, although, as Admiral FitzRoy comments, storm glasses should be fixed outside, while, of course, these barometers were not made for outside use. However, a number of storm glasses were made, particularly by Negretti & Zambra, whom Admiral FitzRoy clearly promotes in his book.

Figure 2.4 shows a storm glass and calibrated thermometer mounted on a mahogany frame for external use (obviously for under cover). The liquid, as so often happens, has partly evaporated. The glass tube is etched with the words 'Fair' towards the bottom, 'Change' in the middle and 'Stormy' towards the top. Since the thermometer is a Meteorological Office numbered thermometer (no. 7794), made by Negretti & Zambra, it is interesting to ponder whether this was considered a serious instrument at the time. It may perhaps be a later adaptation of two separate instruments – a thermometer and a storm glass.

Figure 2.5 also illustrates a thermometer and a storm glass, probably circa 1920. The black-finished, wooden case is inscribed 'Stormy', 'Change' and 'Fair' along the length of the storm glass. Figure 2.6 is a boxwood-mounted thermometer with storm glass by Joseph Davis & Co., Fitzroy Works, London, SE. The scale is inscribed 'Fair', 'Change' and 'Rain' alongside the storm glass, which has only the crystals remaining.

Figure 2.7 is a storm glass mounted on oak, with ivory scales, each engraved 'Fair', 'Change' and 'Rain'; again, the camphor has evaporated and just some residual crystals remain in the base. A number of other models appear from time to time as separate instruments. Figure 2.8 is an example of an American 'Admiral Barometer' utilising the same idea in a very crude mount. Figure 2.9 shows the reverse with the remains of the instructions. These read as follows:

'Admirals – new cottage barometer or storm glass and thermometer combined

'Is composed of various chemicals and is very accurate to foretell the changes of the weather, particularly high wind, storms and tempest. It can be carried about or shaken up without fear of injury.

'Directions: First, if the weather is to be fine the substance of

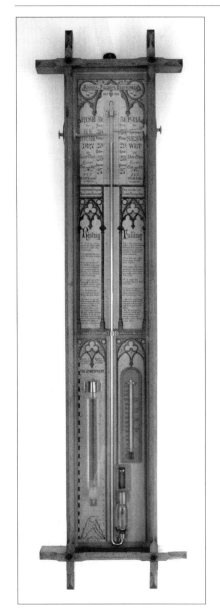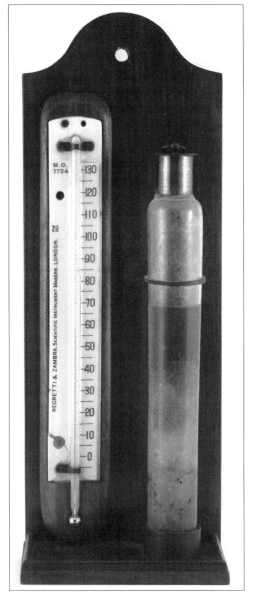

Left, Figure 2.3: Basic style of domestic Admiral FitzRoy barometer, circa 1890.

Right Figure 2.4: Mahogany-mounted storm glass and thermometer for outside use, circa 1875.

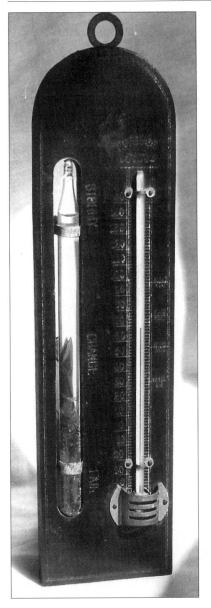 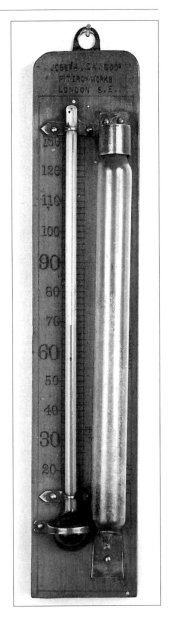

Left, Figure 2.5: Thermometer and storm glass, circa 1920.
Right, Figure 2.6: Thermometer and storm glass by Joseph Davis and Co., circa 1880.

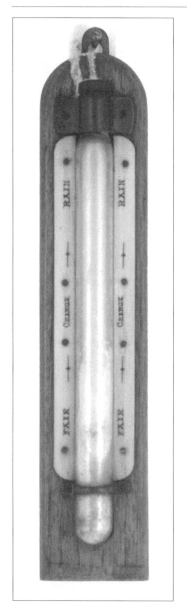
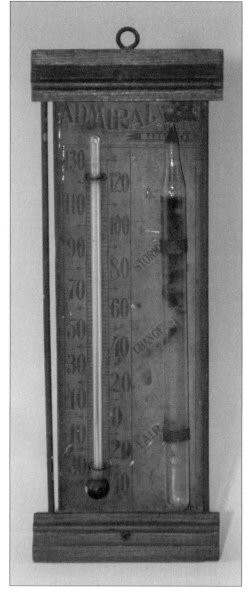

Figure 2.7: Oak-mounted storm glass with ivory scales, circa 1870.
Figure 2.8: American 'Admiral Barometer' storm glass, circa 1920.

Figure 2.9: Instructions on reverse of 'Admiral Barometer' featured in Figure 2.8.

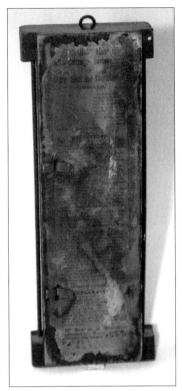

the composition will remain at the bottom and the liquid will be clear.

'Second, previous to rain the substance will rise vertically and the liquid will clear with small particles floating about.

'Third, before a storm or high wind the substance will be partly at the top and will have a feathery appearance and the liquid will be heavy and in termination. In this it will usually clear 24 hours before the weather change.

'Fourth, in winter generally the substance will rise rather high; in snowy weather or white frost it will be with small stars in motion.

'Fifth, in summer the weather being warm and dry, the substance will be quite low.

Sixth, to know which quarter the wind or storm comes from you will observe the substance will lie closer to the bottle on the opposite side to that from which the storm or wind comes.

'N.B. If this instrument is to be of service it should be noted at stated periods similar to the ordinary barometer. Care must be taken to hang it in a room or place of medium temperature as it is in some degree acted upon by extremes of heat or cold. In summer time it is best out of doors where the sun does not act upon it. It works better in a place where there is a current of air than in a close room.

'Before hanging it up shake it well so that the ingredients are well mixed. It also acts better if shaken up occasionally, say every two or three months. Do not hang it in the sun.

'Explanation: if in use the mercury in the thermometer gets separated in transportation a sudden jerk or knock on the bottom of the instrument will bring it together again. In cases of a new glass tube or thermometer glass wants to be put on, take a large blade of a pocket knife, pry off with care the bands or pieces and remove them.

'Beware of worthless imitations. None genuine without the above trade mark. Price 2 Dollars.'

Over the years many recipes have been produced for making storm glasses and, as FitzRoy states in his *Weather Book*, 'There are many imitations, more or less incorrectly made.' Most of these recipes are impossible to make, or are unclear in terms of the measurement of the ingredients. Occasionally, reference is made to the sealing of the glass tube, which is normally a cork with melted sealing wax over the top. This is the cause of many tubes drying up: over the years the cork shrinks, or the item is laid down, which swells the cork and melts the sealing wax. With a small gap the liquid content evaporates. Occasionally, instructions state that a miniature aperture should be made through the seal with a red-hot needle. Whilst this would indeed render the device subject to atmospheric changes, it would, of course, mean that the liquid would evaporate in a relatively short number of years. We make our own storm glasses hermetically sealed at Merton, and, as some of the illustrations have shown, these are the ones that often last longest.

We are fortunate to have surviving in the Public Record Office information from the Board of Trade Meteorological Department in the form of some interesting dialogue between Admiral FitzRoy and the instrument makers, Negretti & Zambra. In a letter from Negretti & Zambra to Admiral FitzRoy, dated 30 August 1861 (PRO BJ7/38 89249 [v]), they explain the 'storm glass' liquid that Admiral FitzRoy had seen. The letter reads:

'Sir,

In reply to your favour of today we beg to give you the method adopted, and the formula employed for making the Storm Glasses, as nearly as we can, – a great deal depending on manipulation whilst preparing a quantity of fluid for a batch of instruments – Our general formula is as follows and that adhered to in making your instruments.

Mixture No. 1	Mixture No. 2
Mix in a Winchester Quart Bottle	Mix in a Winchester Pint Bottle
10 ozs of Camphor	5 Drams Nitrate of Potash
20 ozs of Spirits of Wine	5 Drams Salammoniac
	20 ozs of Water

The solution No. 2 is then carefully filtered and poured slowly into the camphor solution No. 1 (well agitating the bottle during the mixing) until the camphor is precipitated to a depth of about one third of the solution in bottle No. 1 – the fluid must be well shaken and allowed to stand a few days, – if on inspection the white precipitate does not indicate about one third or fourth, pour into it a small quantity of distilled water, this will throw down more camphor – should there be too much precipitate then add more spirits of wine which will dissolve camphor and so continue until the large bottle you are using is one good large wind glass [storm glass] (it is then when found satisfactory poured into smaller bottles for use). The bottle of fluid from which your glasses were filled we think you saw in our Counting house one day whilst being prepared – it is now exhausted and we shall prepare some more specially for those you ordered yesterday.

We remain Sir
Yours respectfully
Negretti & Zambra'

In FitzRoy's reply of 31 August 1861 to Messrs Negretti & Zambra (PRO BJ7/38 89249 [vi]) he writes 'regarding the formula which Negretti & Zambra use for electric "storm glasses" I have fully proved they are *not* but I have ascertained that they are so regularly influenced by the *electrical* conditions of *air* (*around them* for some hours) that to *believers* in the *plus tension* of polar currents, and *minus* condition of their opposite, are tropical ones – microscopical examination of the mixture when in *hermetically* sealed glass tubes – *fixed* – (not disturbed in the least) placed in free air in or out of doors, shaded and not exposed to sun or fire rays – either direct or radiated – will afford unerring indication of the approach, or continuance of polar, or tropical winds – or a combination of them – inclining to one or the other.'

It is plain that FitzRoy believed that the storm glass was a weather indicator of some merit. In PRO BJ7/38 89249, FitzRoy drafts the following letter:

'Mr Potter – agent for the sale of government charts and other publications at 31 Poultry, London, was formerly acquainted with an Italian named "Malacredi" who first made these so-called storm glasses in England about 40 years ago. Rear Admiral FitzRoy thinks they are affected by electricity and by temperature and not by light alone as he has had them in dark cases as well as in the light. The sun's rays or those of heat from fire act immediately on the composition but these effects are additional to what seem to be normal occurrences of electrical conditions of atmosphere, varying with the preponderance of polar (positive) or tropical (less positive or negative) currents of air.'

This was written on 11 July 1861 as a draft of a letter to Negretti & Zambra. It is in FitzRoy's own hand and obviously forms part of a draft of a communication on the subject, although it does not clearly identify when storm glasses were first made.

In another draft letter by FitzRoy (PRO BJ7/331 89180), undated, although from around the same time, he says: 'respecting the camphor glass, you will find my later published opinions in the Board of Trade, the tenth number of papers and the "Weather Book" published by Longmans privately, I think it affected by the electrical condition of atmosphere and useful as an indicator in connection with other instruments but *not*, alone.'

Investigations by FitzRoy into the origins of the storm glass are tantalisingly brief. In his *Weather Book*, he states that storm glasses have been around for over a hundred years, but nowhere so far have

I found evidence in FitzRoy's research of how he came to this conclusion. His 1861 research had obviously not discovered this fact but, as he was a perfectionist in all he did, I am confident that Admiral FitzRoy would not have stated this fact had it not been his firm belief.

In another surviving handwritten note by FitzRoy (PRO BJ7/38 89249 [iii]) he drafts a letter to Mr Potter asking the name of the Italian who first made and used storm glasses, whom Mr Potter apparently remembered many years ago, and in what year. So it appears that Admiral FitzRoy was discussing with Mr Potter his knowledge of the origins of the storm glass, and it is from him that the earliest makers in England have been attributed to Malacredi. They were probably made before this time but the evidence is not available.

Admiral FitzRoy was resolute in his opinion that storm glasses change in appearance due to electrical charges or tensions in the air, according to the wind coming from the polar or tropical regions, but other authorities give different opinions of the storm glass – frequently that it doesn't work. Its effectiveness, however, may depend greatly on the manufacture of the storm glass and the consistency of the liquid within it.

It is possible that modern substitutes are not as good as the original ingredients. We have searched widely to get the various chemicals and feel that we have made a satisfactory mixture at Merton. On a number of occasions, visitors to the Barometer World Museum have told us how, as children, they saw large camphor bottles outside opticians and that these were taken down in advance of anticipated German bombing during the Second World War. Very few of these ever returned, although I believe that some were displayed for a short time.

A. A. Cook, in *Weather* (issue 21, 1966: 34), writes in the 'Letters to the Editor' section that, as a boy in Whitby in August 1919, he remembers regularly observing a FitzRoy storm glass outside an optician's shop with the legend stating that white spots in motion indicate storm. He recalls his surprise and excitement at seeing these spots – he thinks it was 28 August – and that at the time the sky was clouding over, all the seagulls were flying inland, and later that day a gale with heavy rain blew up from the north-east, causing very rough seas. This continued throughout the following night, the wind later backing to north and north-west.

In the same magazine, D. I. Wicker confirms the effectiveness of

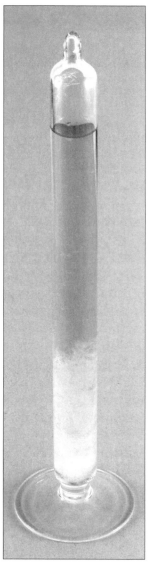

Left, Figure 2.10: Framed storm glass by Barometer World Ltd, Merton, Devon.

Right, Figure 2.11: Free-standing storm glass for window sill by Barometer World Ltd, Merton, Devon.

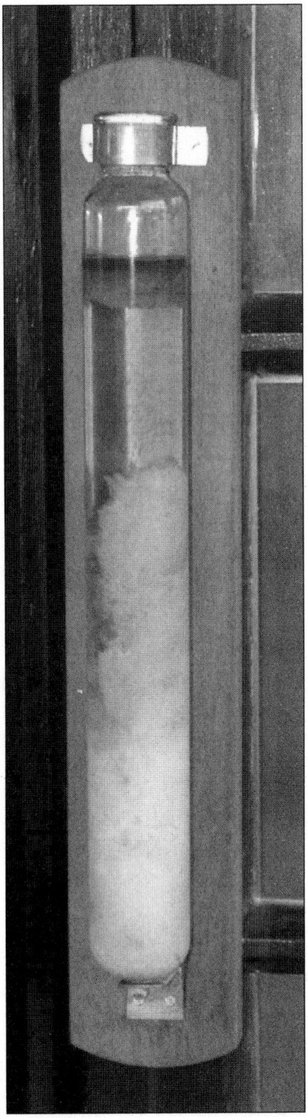

Figure 2.12: Large outdoor storm glass.

storm glasses, and, like Admiral FitzRoy, I too believe they warrant further investigation into the real causes of the observed changes in the liquid. However, this is hampered by the exceptionally high costs of serious scientific study and by variation in the recipes available for storm glasses. If any chemists or physicists would like to rise to the challenge, please contact me.

While some descriptions suggest that the storm glass tube should be open to atmospheric pressure, and indeed many people consider that this is how they work, storm glasses are normally totally sealed; otherwise they dry up. Edward Sebastian Arrighi, in his patent of 1909 (see Appendix), declares his invention of a storm glass made in a glass container in the shape of an electric light bulb, but with flattened sides or convex or concave sides of thin glass so that air pressure reacts internally, the glass sides being flexible enough to do this. This would also, of course, give any temperature or electrical influences a greater surface area for the crystals to respond to more quickly. I have not come across any examples of this patent surviving, but the idea is quite clever and may make a difference.

Figure 2.10 shows a decoratively framed storm glass, available from Barometer World in Devon, which carries on the intriguing mystery of these weather glasses. Figure 2.11 shows a free-standing storm glass designed to be placed on a north-facing window sill to receive the best effect of temperature change and electrical charges from the elements. Figure 2.12 shows a large storm glass, measuring 16 inches high by 2 inches wide, which I have mounted outside under cover on a north-facing window for the purposes of further observation.

3 Shark Oil Barometers

It is possible that there is a link between the storm glasses or bottles available in Britain and the use of shark oil barometers in Bermuda. Bermuda was settled in its early days mostly by travellers from Barnstaple in North Devon, who may have been aware of the weather-predicting features of the storm glass and in time noticed shark liver oil behaving in a similar manner.

According to some sources, the early settlers in Bermuda used shark oil for burning lamps and have been using them as weather predictors for nearly three hundred years. However, despite asking the museum and various other bodies in Bermuda, no evidence from early manuscripts has been forthcoming; so it is likely that this view is based on local folklore, handed down from generation to generation.

It is with particular thanks to the visitors to Barometer World over the years who have mentioned shark oil barometers that my interest was sparked to research this topic. With the assistance of W. Keith Hollis, a Bermuda Islander, I have been supplied with numerous articles and information. However, there is a tremendous scarcity of genuine scientific information. Most of the information we have is accumulated folklore, but even so we can come to some general conclusions.

A shark oil barometer is the oil from the liver of a shark contained in a glass bottle and normally hung outside. Figure 3.1 shows one of our shark oil barometers at Merton. According to George Rushe, in his book *Your Bermuda: All You Need to Know about our Island Home* (1995: 108), 'Scientists who have studied the action of this "barometer" admit that it is accurate but are not certain why or how it works.' So it seems there is at least some tenuous proof that it might work, although hardly scientific-backed research.

Over the past thirty or forty years, the one man who perhaps qualifies to be the expert on Bermudan shark oil barometers is Gerald Smith. W. Keith Hollis had the pleasure of knowing him and many times consulted him for a forecast, usually in the middle of the week for the coming Saturday afternoon yacht club race. On one memorable

Figure 3.1: Shark oil barometer.

occasion he was informed by Gerald Smith, after he had checked his oil, that he would be well advised to set his small flat mainsail the forthcoming weekend, as he saw a front coming through on Saturday afternoon at about 3 pm. He further stated that the wind would quickly swing to the north-west when the front came through and that it would blow like the devil for a couple of hours. He was absolutely correct: the front did come through mid-afternoon on the Saturday and there were a number of dis-masted yachts in the fleet. W. Keith Hollis, having set his small flat mainsail, came through very well indeed. But then, even our weather forecasters get it right from time to time!

According to Thatcher Adams, in a published letter to the editor of the *Royal Gazette*, 9 August 1970, 'Some 40-odd variations have been observed consistent with the weather in a given flask of shark oil.' Figure 3.2 shows six possible forecasts, but I am particularly indebted again to W. Keith Hollis for the illustrations given in Figures 3.3–3.8, which are taken from his own old shark oil barometer. Figure 3.3 shows a definite peak of wax formation in the centre of the wax base. At 6 am on the 9 September 2002 subtropical storm 'Gustav' was located at north 31.7, west 73.4, travelling north-west at 10 mph. Local conditions in Bermuda were heavy overcast with light rain and strong, south-west winds, moving south-east 25–30 knots. Figure 3.4 shows the oil clearing after hurricane 'Gustav' had moved further away. Local weather conditions showed signs of improving. Figure 3.5 shows wax formation on the south-eastern side of the bottle. At this time (20 September 2002) there was a disrupted and unsettled band of weather between the Bahamas and Bermuda away to the south-east of Bermuda: weak, low pressure to the south-east of Bermuda, winds 12–18 knots, scattered showers, occasional thunderstorms with a temperature of 82°F. Figure 3.6 (21 September 2002) shows solid wax; the local weather was heavy rain, wind from the south up to 25 knots, generally poor and not suitable for boating. Figure 3.7 (23 September 2002, 6.30 pm) shows the shark oil to be almost clear with a few suspended dots of wax crystal in the oil column and a very small amount of solid wax, perhaps 1/8 inch thick on the bottom of the bottle. The tropical storm 'Kyle' was 765 miles south-east of Bermuda, the local weather good. Figure 3.8 (30 September 2002, 4.45 pm) shows the shark oil beginning to clear. Locally, there was a storm hurricane watch, winds from north-east 25 knots, gusting to 45 knots. There were thunderstorms with isolated showers, poor

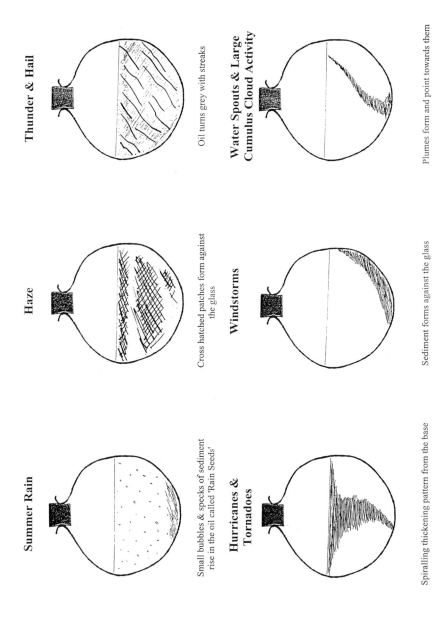

Thunder & Hail

Oil turns grey with streaks

Haze

Cross hatched patches form against the glass

Summer Rain

Small bubbles & specks of sediment rise in the oil called 'Rain Seeds'

Water Spouts & Large Cumulus Cloud Activity

Plumes form and point towards them

Windstorms

Sediment forms against the glass towards the wind

Hurricanes & Tornadoes

Spiralling thickening pattern from the base

Figure 3.2: Six possible forecasts using a shark oil barometer.

Left, Figure 3.3: Wax peak formation in the centre of the shark oil.
Right, Figure 3.4: Shark oil clearing after a hurricane.

Left, Figure 3.5: Wax formation on the side of the bottle.
Right, Figure 3.6: Shark oil looking like solid wax.

Left, Figure 3.7: Almost clear shark oil with suspended spots.
Right, Figure 3.8: Shark oil beginning to clear.

visibility, the temperature was 83°F, and storm 'Kyle' was about 180 nautical miles south of Bermuda. The local forecast was that 'Kyle' would pass Bermuda to the east by mid-week.

It is therefore clearly proved that the shark oil does indeed react to weather conditions, but, as with most types of predictor, it also involves the skill of the forecaster to interpret the patterns. This skill is a combination of local knowledge, wind direction, temperature, time of year, and so on. With over forty types of pattern, some very fine variations can obviously be observed and an accumulation of many years knowledge is important for the successful use of shark oil barometers.

How to Make a Shark Oil Barometer

I have occasionally been asked if we sell shark oil barometers, but the reader will appreciate the impracticality of providing them, not to mention the questionable practice of hunting sharks for their oil should the barometers prove to have worldwide popularity. My own initial search found, via a company in Bermuda, the tourist shark oil barometer illustrated in Figure 3.9. It is mounted on cedar wood and is a typical small tourist gimmick. These types of phials are often made with (if any) shark oil adulterated with vegetable oils and cooking fats and are totally useless for the purposes of the serious barometer enthusiast.

My next move was to try to locate shark liver, and with the help of a West Country fisherman I managed to obtain one. This was duly hung up, the oil dripping out, and I successfully gathered about 6 fluid ounces of a rather yellowy, opaque oil. Having placed it on our small, flat-roofed shed, we began to notice some changes. However, one stormy night it actually blew off and smashed to the ground. Utter dismay at

Figure 3.9: Shark oil barometer as sold to tourists in Bermuda.

all our efforts in extracting the oil wasted, but yet another lesson learned.

The general consensus of opinion on shark liver oil barometers is that the shark should be caught at the end of the season, around August/September when it has fed well on oil-rich food, such as mackerel, and it should be caught on the approach of a full moon, or within a week prior to it. The shark's liver must be pure white or a pinkish milk white; dark livers are of no use. The type of shark most preferred is the puppy shark, better known as the Galapagos shark (*Carcharhinus galapagensis*), although often used also is the dusky shark (*Carcharhinus obscurus*). The Galapagos shark, not easy to catch around Bermudan shores these days, yields a whiter oil; the dusky sharks a more orange-coloured oil. Once the liver is obtained it can be frozen, as this does not destroy the natural ingredients.

To extract the oil, the time-honoured method in Bermuda was to hang the liver in the sun, cutting the ends of the lobes of the liver, and allowing the oil to drip into a jar. The Bermudan sunshine would accomplish this in a few days – it would also attract a number of flies and no doubt other vermin! A more scientific method, often preferred these days, would be to heat the liver in a double saucepan so that it is not cooked but the oil is extracted out. This is explained by Thatcher Adams, in the *Royal Gazette,* 9 August 1970: 'It does not matter how the oil is extracted provided the fatty substance, squalene, is not destroyed by cooking; for example, butter may be heated to a clear fat, cooled again to its usual state. However, if the butter is cooked or over-heated it will brown and upon cooling will not return to its usual state, because the fat has been cooked. The livers can also be placed in a large gallon size jar and placed in the sun. However, there is some extreme smell after a number of days when opened.'

Once the oil is successfully extracted, it is essential to filter it by warming and passing it at least three times through clean muslin. Then it should be placed in a clean, clear, dry flask and hermetically sealed. Gerald Smith suggests a rounded flask or bottle as the best shape, but traditionally any clear bottle is used, such as a clear rum bottle. The container should be half filled with the oil. Some mention is made of hanging the bottle upside down, although no operational benefit would probably be gained. The oil matures over the years and improves in its operational ability. W. Keith Hollis has a shark oil barometer which is well over thirty years old, and records of oil barometers over forty years old are well known in Bermuda.

Thatcher Adams suggests that a good method of mounting the flask is to make a shelf on a narrow slat of wood and screw the slat to a post or wall, painting the stand white and fastening the neck of the flask or bottle to the vertical slat with wire or rot-proof string, with a nail either side of the bottle to stop it being blown around during windy weather. In Bermuda, the preferred location is on a south-west corner of the house, with an unobstructed view of the sky to the east, south and west and to the sky above. The Bermudans prefer to put their shark oil barometers in full sun, while our storm glasses in Britain would normally be placed on a north-facing wall away from the sun.

I was contacted by a Mr Young from Scotland who was a member of the Meteorological Office from 1940, originally in Bermuda until 1982. Apparently they tried making shark oil barometers scientifically in the early 1940s, but the barometers, he says, never worked. They were always told that the St David Islanders made the best ones. His instructions were to hang the barometer outside but not in the sun, so the argument will continue for many years to come. Thatcher Adams has also heard of turtle oil being used in the south but this is not proven.

How Do Shark Oil Barometers Work?

There are a number of suggestions to explain why a shark oil barometer reacts and changes as it does. The majority of people consider it to be just an effect of temperature, but mention is occasionally made of atmospheric electrics and the most comprehensive reason so far comes from Thatcher Adams: 'infra-red irradiation is the driving force causing the variations and that squalene, the chemical that the shark manufactures in its liver, which is a double-bonded, super-saturated hydro carbon, $C_{30}H_{50}$, has a short scale temperature response: performs as a self-integrating thermometer'.

My own view is that temperature plays a major role, but that electrical disturbances and variations in the atmosphere also play a part. According to the article by Gerald Smith, 'Shark Knows Where the Weather Is', published in the *Sea Frontiers* magazine of the International Oceanographic Foundation (volume 16, no. 3, May–June 1970): 'Shark liver oil is very rich in certain steroidal substances that have the characteristic of altering their solubility in response to very slight changes in temperature.'

Our own research over several years has gone into studying a

31

variety of shark oil barometers suspended outside, and has brought us to the conclusion that, in Britain, the generally lower temperatures mean that the shark oil normally has the appearance of solid wax for most of the year. Interestingly, each shark oil barometer has a different temperature at which it becomes solid, but during periods of brighter, warmer weather they show characteristic patterns and formations.

In our continuing study of these barometers, we will be attempting to thin the shark oil without disturbing its chemical balance. Our first effort has been to use turpentine, which mixes well with oil. So far this has stopped the oil from becoming solid but we may have used too much turpentine as it has affected the oil's temperature range and the oil becomes hazy close to and below freezing. One of our next tests will be to mix amounts of a thinning agent in order to have shark oil barometers that work at the normally lower temperatures that we have in Britain. Another possibility is the use of vegetable oil.

One factor that may make a difference to the oil is the sex of the shark, as the oil of a female shark may have a different chemical balance from that of a male. We now generally receive our oil classified by sex, but it will probably be a number of years before any suitable comparison of data will be available, due to the colder temperatures in Britain and the shortage of quantities of shark oil. Whether shark oil matures and improves as a barometer will also be a fact that only time will tell, and so the research continues. If any readers have a particular scientific knowledge or interest or know of any other similar types of barometer I would be most pleased to hear from them.

4 Weather Predictors and Forecasters

O ver the years I have discovered a number of other unusual weather predictors, which are brought together in this chapter: some not written about previously, others long forgotten. They are all part of man's curious search for weather predicting possibilities. One that I have been unable to obtain a photograph of (for which the reader will no doubt be thankful) is a reference in *Weather Lore* by Richard Inwards (first published in 1893), which reads: 'When the locks of the Navajoes turn damp in the scalp house surely it will rain.' This is no doubt quite true, as they would probably act as a simple hygrometer.

In the autobiography of a doctor living in Labrador, Canada, at the beginning of the twentieth century, *The Story of a Labrador Doctor* by Wilfred Thomason Grenfell, is a description of another unusual barometer: 'Nevertheless, today as a medical man one is startled to see a fox's or wolf's head suspended by a cord from the centre, and to learn that it will always twist the way from which the wind is going to blow. One man had a barometer of this kind hanging from his roof, and explained that the peculiar fact was due to the nature of the animals, which in life always went to windward of others; but if you had a seal's head similarly suspended, it would turn from the wind, owing to the timid character of that creature.' Figure 4.1 shows a suspended fox's skull, which is just as reliable.

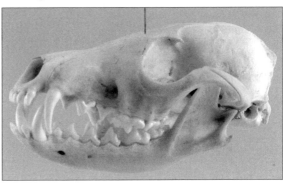

Figure 4.1: A fox skull wind predictor.

Other strange weather predictors are frogs! In *The Lancet* of April–September 1829, we read: *'Zoological Weather Glass*: At Schwitzengen, in the post-house, we witnessed an amusing application of zoological knowledge, for the purpose of prognosticating the weather. Two frogs, of the species *Rana arborea*, are kept in a glass jar about eighteen inches in height, and six inches in diameter, with the depth of three or four inches of water at the bottom, and a small ladder reaching to the top of the jar. On the approach of dry weather the frogs mount the ladder, but when wet weather is expected they descend into the water. These animals are of bright green, and in their wild state here climb the trees in search of insects, and make a peculiar singing noise before rain. In the jar they get no other food than now and then a fly, one of which, we are assured, would serve a frog for a week, though it will eat from six to twelve in a day if it can get them.'

This is not the first reference I have come across regarding frogs. It is quite well known that in Germany a type of frog was kept in a glass of some type and predicted the weather by the sounds it made. One would hope that it was fed on more than just one fly a week!

A curious type of predictor (Figure 4.2), tucked away in a display cabinet at Dunster Castle in Somerset, owned by the National Trust, consists of a tapering board of wood with a hygrometer at the top, thermometer and a calculating dial beneath. It is called a 'Hunting Scentometer' and has 'patent pending' on it, but it is most likely a type of 'Pollard Scentometer', designed by Budgett. With the help of the Patent Office at Newport, I have discovered that this was Hubert Maitland Budgett of Oxford, who filed three provisional specifications as follows:

405,694 Patent Specification Application date 12 August 1932, no. 22,611/32
Application date 12 August 1932, no. 22,612/32
Application date 29 July 1933, no. 21,395/33
One Complete Left, 31 July 1933
Complete accepted, 12 February 1934

In this he describes a portable apparatus in the form of a walking stick, shooting stick, umbrella, rod or frame hinged jointly or telescopically for holding one or more thermometers in the ground and one or more thermometers in the air for the purpose of comparing the temperatures of the earth and air with the object of determining

Figure 4.2: A 'Pollard Scentometer', circa 1935.

Left, Figure 4.3: American pocket weather forecaster by Irving P. Crick, 1949

Right, Figure 4.4: Reverse of weather forecaster shown in Figure 4.3.

whether the scent conditions are good or bad. The term 'scent' here refers to the trail or smell left by quarry pursued by sporting dogs or the like. No doubt his design altered and this one at Dunster Castle is a variation of it.

Figures 4.3 and 4.4 (the reverse) show a rare item found through on-line auction. It is a weather guide made from aluminium, with a suspension hook and compass, showing illustrations of different cloud formations. The instructions are as follows:

'To Forecast

1 Turn printed arrow into view:
      Red in summer
      Blue in winter
2 Carefully observe entire sky.
3 Select picture and description best matching your observation.
4 Determine the direction from which the wind is blowing. If calm or very light use west.
5 Turn arrow to wind direction opposite selected sky picture.
6 Read forecast shown in window.'

I presume it was designed as a pocket-forecasting device, although you would need rather large pockets! It has copyright with patent pending in 1949 from Pasadena, California, Irving P. Crick, PhD.

Keen meteorologists, who have the benefit of a house with a cellar, may like to build a brine barometer, as detailed in an article by P. R. Corbyn in *Weather* (September 1967). Figure 4.5 shows an illustration of such a barometer; the liquid is brine to prevent it freezing in winter, and it is coloured to make it more noticeable. It also has an air trap to contain bubbles of air, which diffuse up the tube towards the lower pressure.

On 28 November 1885 George R. Primrose wrote to the Royal Meteorological Society, who were then at 30 Great George Street, Westminster West, as follows:

'Gentlemen,
Herewith is a rough plan of an Electric Barometer, which I have devised to register over one wire at long distances continuously, or at intervals as desired. If such an instrument is sufficiently novel to deserve the notice of scientific observers, and you think

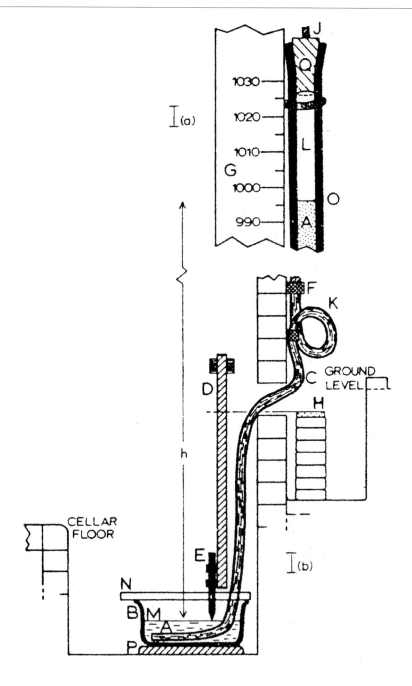

Figure 4.5: Drawing of a 'brine' barometer, 1967.

it is worthwhile for me to proceed further in the matter, I shall be very greatly obliged by hearing from you on the subject. The second modification of the same principle appears to be a more simple and perhaps desirable arrangement.

I remain, Gentlemen,
Your obediant servant
Geo. R. Primrose'

With his communication he sent the 'rough sketches' given in Figures 4.6 and 4.7, showing an elaborate arrangement of electro-magnet wires and gears connected to a mercury barometer. It looks rather similar to a pinball table and is certainly quite novel. I can only assume that the proposal never went very much further, but the drawings, which are illustrated in Figure 4.8, were printed in the *Transactions of the Royal Scottish Society of Arts* in the following year, 1886. It appears that the device was intended for recording pressure at great heights where the weather and conditions made personally travelling to the tops of mountains very impractical for any length of time.

Figure 4.9 shows a Mitchel patent barometer of 1863 (see Appendix). It consists of an aneroid-type bellows or capsule, which is not visible, filled with an alcohol or suitable liquid, having a thermometer-type glass tube attached to it, which is visible, and a chamber at the top with air or gas in it. The principle is that, as the air pressure increases or decreases, the chamber, being thin and flexible, will compress or open and vary the volume of liquid, which is indicated by the level going up and down in the glass tube. Only a few of these instruments have survived, one being in Edinburgh Museum reserve stock, supplied or made by Henderson. The one illustrated, which is in a wooden frame, carries the letters H and B boldly marked on it, which could indicate some form of advertising item, and was sold or made by R. H. G. Wilson, 12 Wilson Street, Gray's Inn, London. Another, by Henry Hughes of 59 Fenchurch St, London, is illustrated in Figure 4.10 with engraved ivory scales. They do not seem to survive in a working condition probably due to the glass and metal seal.

Figure 4.11 illustrates a balance barometer, patented by Henry Mapple (see Appendix). It is simply designed to have a corrugated cone-shaped capsule, which is evacuated (currently missing), resting on a balance, and as the pressure increases or decreases the cone

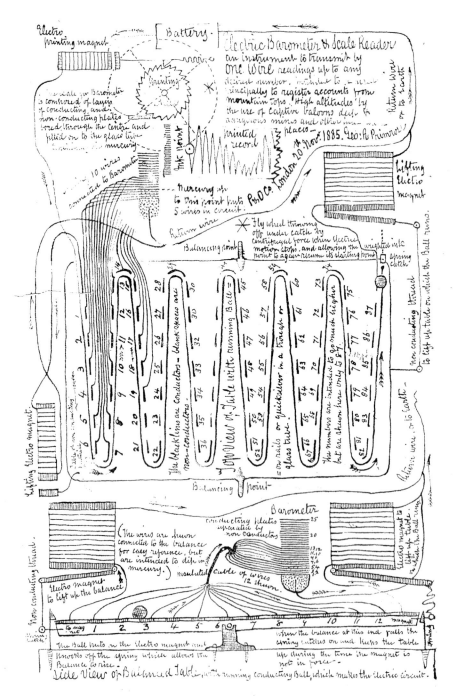

Figure 4.6 : Primrose Electric Barometer, 1885, drawing 1.

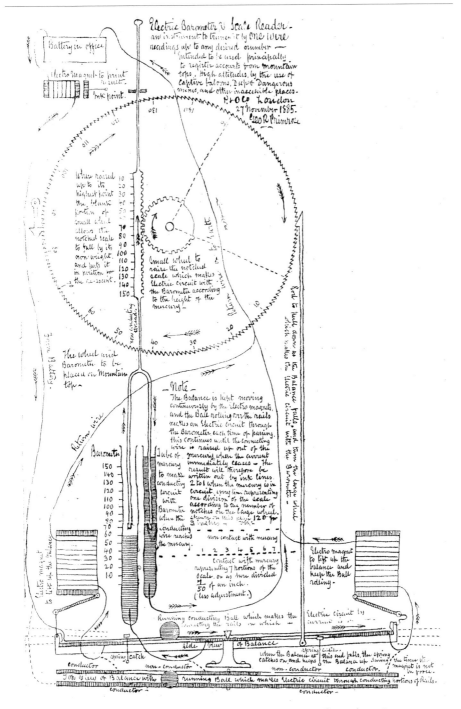

Figure 4.7: Primrose Electric Barometer, 1885, drawing 2.

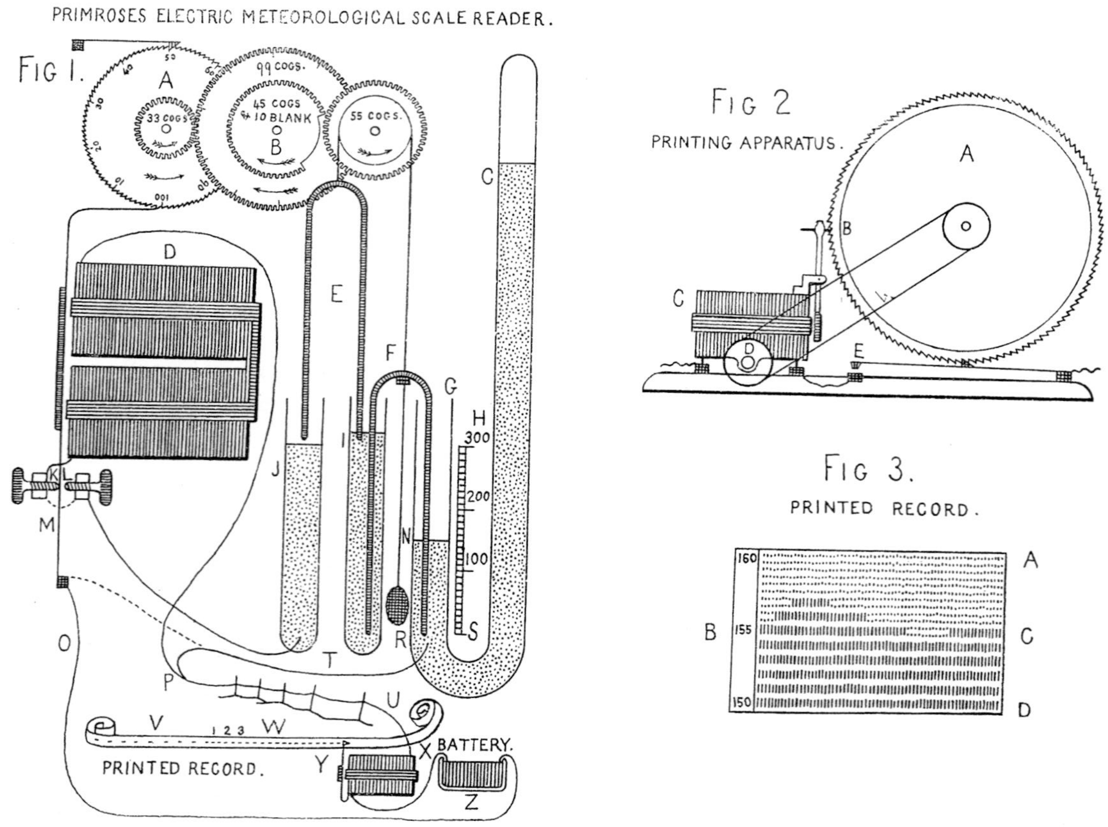
PRIMROSES ELECTRIC METEOROLOGICAL SCALE READER.
FIG I.
A
33 COGS
99 COGS.
45 COGS
& 10 BLANK
B
55 COGS.
C
D
E
F
G
H
300
200
100
I
J
K
L
M
N
O
P
R
S
T
U
V
1 2 3
W
X
BATTERY.
Y
Z
PRINTED RECORD.
FIG 2
PRINTING APPARATUS.
A
B
C
D
E
FIG 3.
PRINTED RECORD.
160
155
150
A
B
C
D

Figure 4.8: Improved Primrose Electric Barometer, 1886.

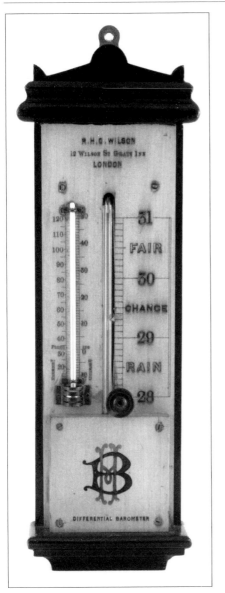 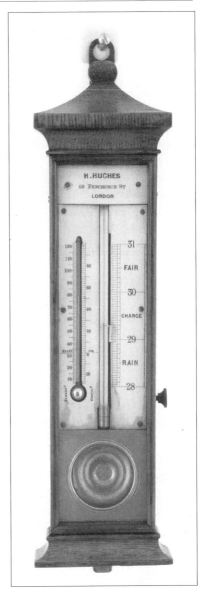

Left, Figure 4.9: Mitchel patent barometer, 1863, inscribed R. H. G. Wilson.
Right, Figure 4.10: Mitchel patent barometer, 1863, by Henry Hughes.

expands and contracts, and thus weight is shifted from one side to the other, and the needle, which is attached to the swinging cradle, moves left and right in front of the scale, which is just visible at the top. There is also a recording hand, which is turned by the knob in the front of the base. It is thought to be the only surviving example of this patent.

Figure 4.12 shows a 'Union Barometer' from America. It consists of a glass tube with a bulb turned up at the base, with mercury partly filling it to trap gas or air in the bulb; the screw at the bottom, visible on the left-hand side, adjusts a thermometer so that the level of the thermometer is lined up with the level in the glass tube. This also moves the vernier indicator on the right-hand side between the words 'Rain' and 'Fair'. The screw at the top is a transporting screw and when tightened stops air pressure reacting on the column of mercury. The case is in stained pine and the scales are silvered brass, and measure 15.5 inches high by 5 inches wide. It probably dates from the late Victorian period and was found in a collection of items of a gentleman in America, where it had been gathering dust for some years.

It is a fact of life that one often regrets not buying particular items at auction, and one such item I now regret was a weather prognosticator that came up for auction several years ago before I became interested in these different varieties of unusual barometer. There are probably only a few surviving. Figure 4.13 shows one that I managed to buy just before this book went to press from a collector in the United States. It is shown with door open and all the dials and text in good order. The few that I have seen or heard about are framed behind a simple glazed door, normally gilded or painted gold and with rosettes in each corner; probably because of the door, they have survived quite well. The one illustrated here has brass engraved hands. Another, which is on display at Snowshill Manor, Snowshill, Broadway, Worcestershire, has wooden hands and may have been produced a little later.

This intriguing weather forecasting item, which was published (printed) by C. Upton, Bookseller, Exeter, and designed by Henry Troke of Topsham, 1831, contains four dials, each of which has hands to be set manually, and indicate probable weather. The top centre dial gives the day of the week and the date of the month and there is an aperture above to show the name of the month. The bottom centre dial has hands to indicate New, Full, First Quarter and Last Quarter phases

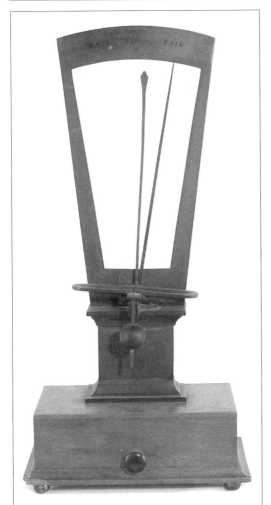 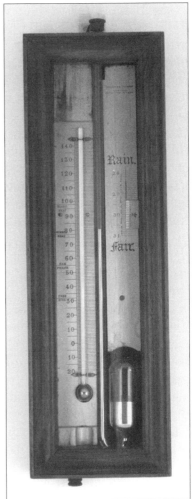

Left, Figure 4.11: Balance barometer by Henry Mapple, 1856.
Right, Figure 4.12: American 'Union Barometer', circa 1890.

of the Moon. The two dials in the centre on the left and right are one for Summer and the other for Winter weather predictions. The hands are engraved with First, Last, Full and New and each one can be pointed to the time of day that these would happen, presumably daily set from charts. The legend at the top states: 'These dials and the accompanying remarks are the result of many years actual observation; the whole being constructed on a due consideration of the attraction of the sun and moon in their several positions respecting the earth; and will by simple inspection show the observer what kind of weather will most probably follow the entrance of the moon into any of her quarters, and that so near the truth as to be seldom or ever found to fail.' At the bottom of the legend it states 'Designed and improved upon the system of the late astronomer Sir Wm Herschel by Henry Troke of Topsham 1831'. The 'sculptur' (perhaps meaning maker) was Roper of Exeter. In my opinion, it is far from simple to read and, as yet, I have not quite broken the 'code' as to how to use it, though I shall continue to research this item.

Some readers may recall the simple small 'toy' known as a 'Cartesian diver', which has been popular on and off over the years. It consists of a small figure, hollow underneath, which is placed in a bottle with a cork in it and mostly filled with water. If the cork is pushed in further, the air pressure inside the bottle increases and the air in the diver reduces under compression and so the diver 'dives' to the bottom of the bottle; when the cork is lifted up, the diver 'floats' back up again. A curious type of barometer based on the Cartesian diver principle is described in volume 24 of *The Philosophical Transcripts*, and is illustrated in Figure 4.14. It appears to be an exceptionally sensitive item. Although perhaps not a very practical type of barometer to operate, it is nevertheless an interesting variation.

Called 'Mr Caswell's Baroscope or Barometer,' it is described in *The Philosophical Transcripts* as follows:

'Suppose ABCD ... is a bucket of water, in which is the baroscope *xrczyosm*, which consists of a body *xrsm*, and a tube *czyo*, which are both concave cylinders, made of tin, or rather glass, and communicating with each other. The bottom of the tube *zy* has a leaden weight to sink it, so that the top of the body may just swim even with the surface of the water by the addition of some grain weights on the top. When the instrument is forced with its mouth downwards, the water ascends into the tube to

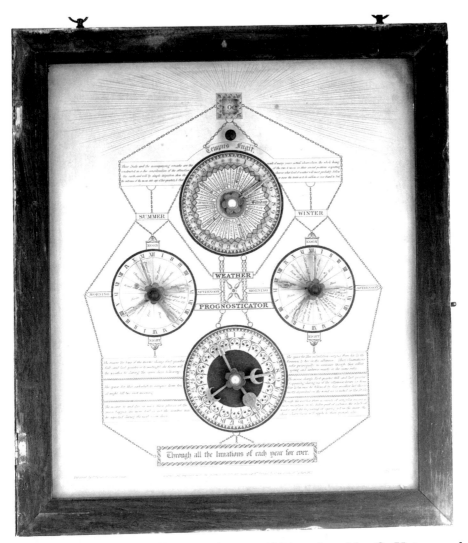

Figure 4.13: Weather Prognosticator, 1831, printed by C. Upton and designed by Henry Troke of Topsham.

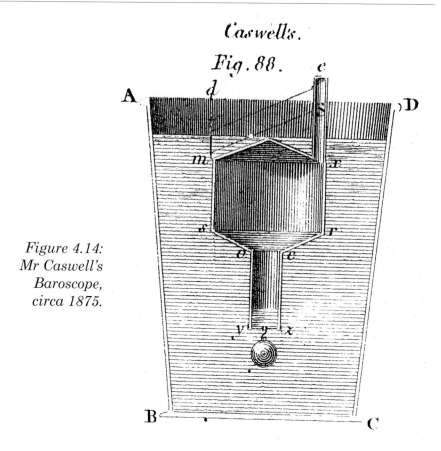

Caswell's.

Fig. 88.

Figure 4.14: Mr Caswell's Baroscope, circa 1875.

the height *yu*. To the top is added a small concave cylinder, or pipe, to keep the instrument from sinking down to the bottom: *md* is a wire: and *mS, de* are two threads oblique to the surface of the water, which perform the office of diagonals: for while the instrument sinks more or less by an alteration in the gravity of the air, where the surface of the water cuts the thread is formed a small bubble, which ascends up the thread while the mercury of the common baroscope ascends, and vice versa. It appears from a calculation that the author makes, that this instrument shows the alterations in the air 1200 times more accurately than the common barometer. He observes, that the bubble is seldom known to stand still even for a minute; that a small blast of wind, which cannot be heard in a chamber, will sensibly make it sink; and that a cloud passing over it always makes it descend, etc.

'While some have been increasing the sensibility of the barometer by enlarging the variations, others have endeavoured to make it more convenient by reducing the length of the tube. M. Amontons, in 1688, first proposed this alteration in the structure of barometers, by joining several tubes to one another, alternately filled with mercury and with air, or some other fluid; and the number of these tubes may be increased at pleasure: but the contrivance is perhaps more ingenious than useful.'

Figure 4.15 shows a modern version we have made of glass.

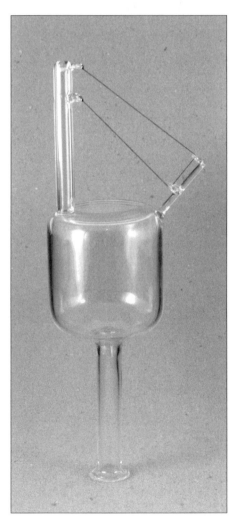

Another type of Cartesian diver barometer is illustrated in Figure 4.16, which was patented in 1884 by David Winstanley (see Appendix). It has a hollow glass bulb open at one end through the glass hook at the bottom and filled so as to trap the right amount of air in it so that it rises up and down with atmospheric pressure changes; the chain attached to it is a clever method of restricting the movement of the bulb to make it of use as a barometer. As the pressure increases the volume of air in the bulb is compressed and so the bulb sinks, but as it does so fewer links of the chain weigh it down so it becomes lighter and only moves a smaller amount; similarly, when the pressure decreases the volume of air trapped in the bulb increases and allows the bulb to rise, but in so doing the chain is lifted and adds weight to the bulb thus restricting the movement somewhat.

Figure 4.15: A modern Caswell Baroscope.

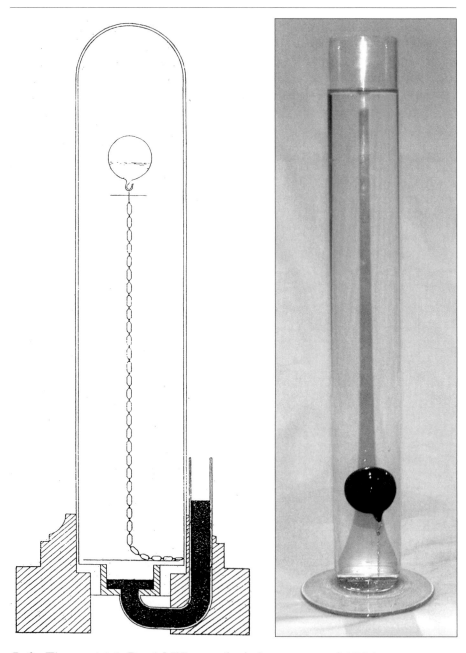

Left, Figure 4.16: David Winstanley's barometer of 1884.
Right, Figure 4.17: Version of Winstanley's barometer made by Barometer World Ltd, Merton, Devon.

Without the chain, the bulb would rise completely and fall completely very easily and be of little use as a barometer. Our own style of this barometer, made somewhat simpler, can be seen in Figure 4.17.

Negretti & Zambra's pocket weather-forecasting device is a well-known calculator, but from the late Victorian era we are fortunate to have surviving in the Meteorological Office Library Records details of Pastorelli's wind and weather indicator illustrated in Figure 4.18. Frank Pastorelli was working up until 1897 and, as it states, this device was intended for the purpose of enabling the general public to comprehend the daily reports of the Meteorological Office.

There have been a number of other weather-forecasting devices. Figure 4.19 shows Pilkington's copyright weather forecaster. It is similar to the Negretti & Zambra forecaster (see my *Aneroid Barometers and their Restoration*, p. 200), although mounted on a rectangular piece of card, and has twenty-two possible forecasts, depending on the barometer reading, the wind direction and the state of the barometer. It is printed in dark blue, red and black on a creamy background. I am uncertain of the exact date but would expect it to be comparable to the Negretti & Zambra forecaster and date from the first quarter of the twentieth century. Pilkington's forecaster is quite a rare item, probably because, being made of cardboard, it has not survived as well as the Negretti & Zambra forecaster.

An earlier forecaster is probably the Hatfield red, white and blue barometrical indicator, illustrated in Figure 4.20. This is printed on cream card with a red circle and blue inner barometer dial and, as stated, it is 'founded on the law of mutual attractions in the distribution of vapour'. This is the only example I have so far seen. The way to use the indicator is described as follows: 'Turn the date on the disc to the Bearing of the Barometer when at the lowest for the month, turn the red hand of the Indicator to that date and the opposite Blue end will show the date of the next bad Weather and the good or still Weather at right Angles of these dates. The intrinsic value of these forecasts is, that when nature weighs herself in the Barometer, we calculate by this Indicator its fair and rough times, for months in advance.'

The Taylor Instrument Companies of Rochester, NY, USA, are known to have produced, along with Short & Mason, barometers that have weather indications according to barometer reading and falling or rising state. Figure 4.21 shows a forecasting device, and not a barometer, based on a more scientific approach, according to wind

PASTORELLI'S WIND AND WEATHER INDICATOR,

AND THE STATIONS OF THE METEOROLOGICAL OFFICE,

Showing the Direction of the Prevalent Winds; their Characteristic Properties and the Weather they Produce.

Intended for the purpose of enabling the general Public to comprehend the Daily Reports of the Meteorological Office. R. H. Scott, M.A., F.R.S., Director.

Suggested by F. PASTORELLI : Designed and Constructed by ANDREW STEINMETZ; Author of "A Manual of Weathercasts," "Everybody's Weather Guide," &c., &c.

I. In judging of the weather, the first thing is to know where barometers stand highest, and where they are lowest. Now, facing the wind blowing at any time there will be lowest barometers on your right and highest on your left.

II. Standing thus, with high pressures on your left, and low pressures on your right *(if these be ascertained)*, then the wind during the day will be in a direction more or less at right angles to a line drawn between the highest and lowest barometrical pressure in front of you.

These points or areas of highest and lowest pressure are given daily in the Weather Report of the Meteorological Office, published in the *Times* newspaper.

III. If we note the area of high and low pressure from day to day, as thus reported, we are enabled to prognosticate the weather that may be impending for a longer period, as follows. The wind has a tendency to *back*, that is, for instance, to shift from N to W ; or to veer regularly, from N to E, according to the shifting of the area of *lowest pressure.* Now, when the wind tends to *back*, we have unsettled weather; but when it veers regularly, the weather is more settled. Therefore, if the area of lowest pressure be irregular in its progression, so will be the weather; if the area *backs*, say from E towards N, then will the wind back, say from W towards S, with continued unsettled weather, and *vice versâ.*

IV. The regular veering of the wind in the Northern Hemisphere, *is with the sun,* forwards, as S, SW, W, NW, N, NE, E, SE, S, not necessarily from point to point, but in that direction.

In the Southern Hemisphere, the regular veering of the wind is reversed, but still *with the sun,* namely, S, SE, E, NE, N, NW, W, SW, S. But here, of course, the lowest barometers will be on the *left* in facing the wind at any time; thus wind S,—then lowest barometers in the E. And the nature of the winds are reversed, that is, N, NW, and NE correspond to S, SW, and SE in the North Hemisphere—S, SW, and SE to N, NW, and NE in the North—more or less, but not completely.

V. The kind of weather caused by the various winds is shown in the margin of the INDICATOR ; and Farmers especially should know that the nature of the *Harvest* depends upon the regularity of the *veering* of the wind throughout the year, but particularly in Spring. Continual *backing* of the wind in Spring is a bad prospect for the harvest, there being always a close relation between the periods of such backings and regular veerings, with good and bad years for the crops—the former resulting in unsettled, stormy weather, as attested by the late Sir John Herschel, from the anemometrical records of Greenwich Observatory.

☞ One of the discs of the pointers of the INDICATOR should be set on the point of lowest pressure, and the other pointer in the direction of the wind from day to day, thus checking results and judging accordingly.

F. PASTORELLI, Scientific Instrument Maker, Manufacturer to the Board of Trade, the Ordnance Select Committee, the Admiralty, and the Government of the Dominion of Canada. 208, PICCADILLY.   Prize Medal awarded for Novel Improvements and superior excellence of work, at the Great Exhibition, 1862.

[ENTERED AT STATIONERS' HALL]   *For further information see Book Edition.*

Figure 4.18: Wind and weather indicator by Frank Pastorelli, circa 1892.

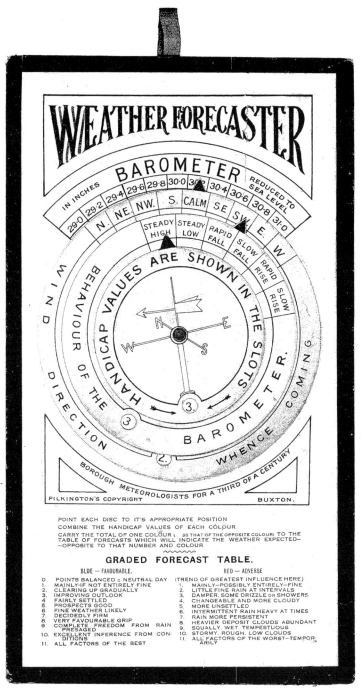

Figure 4.19: Pilkington's Weather Forecaster, circa 1920s.

HATFIELD'S,
RED WHITE AND BLUE
BAROMETRICAL INDICATOR.

THE WAY TO USE IT.

Turn the date on the disc to the Bearing of the Barometer when at the lowest for the month, turn the red hand of the Indicator to that date and the opposite Blue end will show the date of the next bad Weather and the good or still Weather at right Angles of these dates. The intrinsic value of these forecasts is, that when nature weighs herself in the Barometer, we calculate by this Indicator its fair and rough times, for months in advance.

"FOREARMED".

FOUNDED ON THE LAW OF MUTUAL ATTRACTIONS IN THE DISTRIBUTION OF VAPOUR,

CALCULATED FOR TIME BY THE SQUARES OF THE MOON'S ORBIT, RECKONING FROM THE LOWEST

FALL FOR THE MONTH ;

And

Found to be correct by thirty years observations.

———o———

ENT. STA. HALL.

———o———

PRICE HALF-A-CROWN.
Posted free per Post.

"FOREWARNED"

LONDON : Mr. W. HATFIELD, 2, VICTORIA TERRACE, SHEPHERDS' BUSH.
AND CAN BE OBTAINED THROUGH ANY OPTICIAN OR STATIONER.

Figure 4.20: Hatfield's Red, White and Blue Barometrical Indicator, circa 1890s.

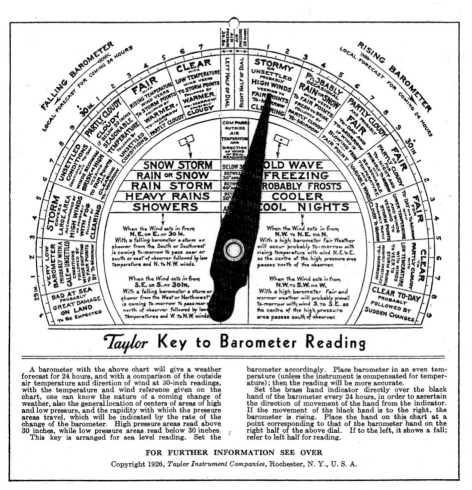

A barometer with the above chart will give a weather forecast for 24 hours, and with a comparison of the outside air temperature and direction of wind at 30-inch readings, with the temperature and wind reference given on the chart, one can know the nature of a coming change of weather, also the general location of centers of areas of high and low pressure, and the rapidity with which the pressure areas travel, which will be indicated by the rate of change of the barometer. High pressure areas read above 30 inches, while low pressure areas read below 30 inches. This key is arranged for sea level reading. Set the barometer accordingly. Place barometer in an even temperature (unless the instrument is compensated for temperature); then the reading will be more accurate.

Set the brass hand indicator directly over the black hand of the barometer every 24 hours, in order to ascertain the direction of movement of the hand from the indicator. If the movement of the black hand is to the right, the barometer is rising. Place the hand on this chart at a point corresponding to that of the barometer hand on the right half of the above dial. If to the left, it shows a fall; refer to left half for reading.

FOR FURTHER INFORMATION SEE OVER

Figure 4.21: Barometer weather indicator by Taylor Instrument Companies, circa 1920s.

direction, barometric reading and direction of change. On the reverse are general indications and altitude adjustments for barometers.

Again from America, we have a curious weather forecaster by Dr Manfred Curry, illustrated in Figure 4.22. It is a plastic moulded item with a compass mounted in its centre and, if the advertising is to be believed, it 'will solve your annoying weather problems'. It contains a chemical material which indicates the degree of moisture in the air by its changing colours – probably a cobalt salt (see chapter 7).

Another, perhaps slightly more scientific, approach is 'The Daily Weather Guide', illustrated in Figure 4.23, which measures 220 mm in diameter. It is a simple cloud-recognition device by D. & K. Bartlett, 'the long-range weather experts'. This particular item was sold for 1s 6d by George Phillip & Son Ltd, 82 Fleet Street, London, and I would suggest that it dates from the 1920s or 1930s. Figure 4.24 shows a simple postcard-type forecasting device, printed in the USA, obviously for promotional purposes: typed at the top (not shown) is 'The industrial bank where the smart money banks'.

Perhaps one of the most natural barometers is the human body. Many older people say that they can tell when it is going to rain because of an ache in their knee or elbow. My own theory is that people suffering from a particular type of arthritis, or painful inflammation in the joints, in the event of a sudden drop in air pressure will find that any dissolved gases in their joints will increase slightly (a similar, but much worse, effect is had when divers ascend too quickly and gas in the blood stream enlarges suddenly, giving them 'the bends'). Any small increase in the size of fluids or gases around sensitive bone or cartilage in the joints could easily give discomfort and pain, possible treatment for which would be immersing in water to increase the pressure. In fact, water immersion has been practised by a number of medical institutes, especially in Russia, although mainly for the symptoms of gout. Figure 4.25 shows what is perhaps a 1920s' cartoon of the 'human barometer'.

Another unusual 'barometer' is my own version of Robert Hooke's Otheometer, which I designed on the basis of a reference in Robert Hooke's diary. In July 1677 he noted: 'It is now very evident that the Otheometer moves directly opposite to the barometer.' In this period, when the mercury barometer had only just been introduced into Britain, Robert Hooke devised what he called an 'Otheometer'. No plans or original instruments survive, but it would certainly have been based on simple barometers of the time, which were mainly liquid

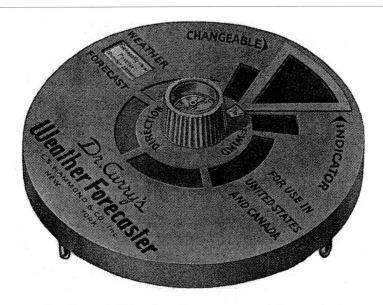

Figure 4.22: Dr Curry's Weather Forecaster, mid-twentieth century.

Figure 4.23: The Daily Weather Guide by D. & K. Bartlett, circa 1920s.

Figure 4.24: Promotional weather forecaster, circa 1950s.

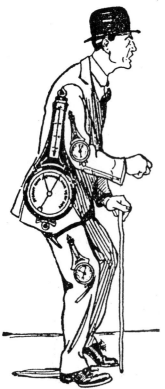

Figure 4.25: A 'human barometer' (source unknown).

and air type weather glasses. 'Othe' comes from the Latin 'to push' and 'meter' is 'to measure', so it is literally a 'push measure': the air pushes down from the opening in the top of the long tube and allows the liquid to go up and down. However, my own model has been improved to reduce temperature effects and has been put with a scale of typical seventeenth-century design. Figure 4.26 shows an example of one, for which we have filed our own patent because of the novel design of temperature control hitherto not patented or used.

Figure 4.26: An 'Otheometer', inspired by Robert Hooke, made by Barometer World Ltd, Merton, Devon.

5 The Tempest Prognosticator

Almost certainly the most bizarre weather-forecasting device ever invented and made was the Tempest Prognosticator or, to give it its full title, 'Atmospheric Electro-magnetic Telegraph Conducted by Animal Instinct'. This incredible device was built by Dr George Merryweather and exhibited at the Great Exhibition at The Crystal Palace in 1851.

George Merryweather was born in 1793 and died on 1 November 1870 of bronchitis. He apparently had a strong inventive urge, and in 1831 described a 'platina' lamp, which could be kept burning for a fortnight on an economical mixture of pure alcohol and whisky, at a cost of only one penny for eight hours. He may have invented other items but he is most famous for the Tempest Prognosticator.

From 'An Essay Explanatory of the Tempest Prognosticator in the building of the Great Exhibition for the works of industry of all nations. Read before the Whitby philosophical society February 27th 1851 by George Merryweather MD, Whitby, the designer and inventor' we are fortunate to have an illustration of the original model (Figure 5.1). Dr Merryweather, obviously aware of the leech's ability to forecast the weather, devised this apparatus so that a bell would ring in advance of severe weather, as a result of the leech's natural desire to rise to the top of a jar or tank in advance of thunderstorms and heavy rain.

Each bottle was designed to have a kind of 'mousetrap affair' at the top. When the leech tried to get to the very top of the bottle it would set the trap off and this would cause a corresponding hammer to ring the bell at the top of the apparatus. Once rung, the hammer would need re-setting so the observer would always know, even after an absence, that the bell had been rung. The more leeches that rang the bell the more a storm was likely. He called his twelve leeches a 'jury'. Dr Merryweather tried to persuade the government to install these 'instruments' around the coast of Britain and instruct people in their use. More fortunately for our modern-day weather forecasters, Admiral FitzRoy's storm barometers were used instead!

Figure 5.1: The Tempest Prognosticator of 1851.

A number of original books and references survive, within which are described the reasons for using leeches to predict the weather, a brief account of how the Prognosticator was made, along with many letters of its trials, which confirm its success. After considerable expense and time, we reproduced a model ready for display on 27 February 2001, 150 years after the original essay was given at Whitby. This full working model can be seen in Figure 5.2. A previous model was made for the Festival of Britain in 1951, and is now housed at Whitby Museum, Pannell Park, Whitby (Figure 5.3). Although very similar in design, it is actually made of wood and papier maché for display purposes only and must have taken some time to make. Our model is a fully working gold-plated version, built on the original concept of a 'pygmy Indian temple' as described by Dr Merryweather. The reader may well consider this weather predictor pure nonsense, but the information in this chapter will, I think, give considerable credence to the claim that leeches can indicate approaching storms.

Dr Merryweather, in his 'Essay of the Tempest Prognosticator', quotes from Hayley's *Life of Cowper* (vol. III, p. 73) to show that the poet William Cowper (1731–1800) kept a leech in a bottle that foretold thunder.

'There is another celebrated poet who has passed a deserved eulogium on the instincts of this little creature, which Cowper communicated in a letter to his cousin, Lady Hesketh, November 10th, 1787, from which I make the following extract: "Mrs Throckmorton carries us tomorrow in her chaise to Chicheley. The event must however be supposed to depend on the elements, at least on the state of the atmosphere, which is turbulent beyond measure. Yesterday it thundered, last night it lightened, and at three this morning I saw the sky red as a city in flames could have made it. I have a leech in a bottle that foretells all the prodigies and convulsions of nature. No, not as you will naturally conjecture, by articulate utterance of oracular notices, but by a variety of gesticulations, which here I have not room to give an account of. Suffice it to say, that no change of weather surprises him, and that in point of the earliest and most accurate intelligence, he is worth all the barometers in the world. None of them all indeed can make the least pretence to foretell thunder, a species of capacity of which he has given the most unequivocal evidence. I gave but sixpence for him, which is a groat more

Figure 5.2: Working model of the Tempest Prognosticator on display at Barometer World, Merton, Devon.

Figure 5.3: 1951 'Festival of Britain' copy of the Tempest Prognosticator on display at Whitby, Yorkshire.

than the market price, though he is in fact or rather would be if leeches were not found in every ditch, an invaluable acquisition." '

A poem often attributed to Edward Jenner (1749–1823), but quite likely written by Erasmus Darwin, Charles Darwin's grandfather, contains reference to the leech as a weather predictor, along with other natural phenomena. It is entitled 'An Excuse for not Accepting the Invitation of a Friend to Make a Country Excursion' and reads:

'The hollow winds begin to blow,
The clouds look black, the glass is low,
The soot falls down, the spaniels sleep,
And spiders from their cobwebs creep.
Last night the sun went pale to bed,
The moon in halos hid her head.
The boding shepherd heaves a sigh,
For, see! The rainbow spans the sky.
The walls are damp, the ditches smell,
Clos'd is the pink-eyed pimpernel.
Hark! How the chairs and tables crack;
Old Betty's joints are on the rack.
Loud quack the ducks, the peacocks cry,
The distant hills are looking nigh.
How restless are the snorting swine –
The busy flies disturb the kine.
Low o'er the grass the swallow wings;
The cricket, too, how loud he sings.
Puss on the hearth with velvet paws
Sits smoothing o'er her whiskered jaws.
Through the clear stream the fishes rise,
And nimbly catch the incautious flies.
The sheep were seen at early light
Cropping the meads with eager bite.
Though June, the air is cold and chill;
The mellow blackbird's voice is still.
The glow-worms, numerous and bright,
Illumed the dewy dell last night.
At dusk the squalid toad was seen
Hopping, crawling o'er the green.
The frog has lost his yellow vest,

65

And in a dingy suit is dress'd.
The leech, disturbed, is newly risen
Quite to the summit of his prison.
The whirling winds the dust obeys,
And in the rapid eddy plays.
My dog, so altered in his taste,
Quits mutton bones on grass to feast.
And see yon rooks, how odd their flight,
They imitate the gliding kite,
Or seem precipitate to fall,
As if they felt the piercing ball.
'Twill surely rain – I see with sorrow,
Our jaunt must be put off to-morrow.'

Of particular interest for the Weather Prognosticator, of course, is the line: 'The leech, disturbed, is newly risen / Quite to the summit of his prison.'

Leeches are closely related to earthworms, and it is often said that if many earthworms appear this precedes rain. An article printed in *Weather* (July 1967, vol. 22, no. 7, p. 288), under the title 'Observations on the leech worm, by a gentleman who kept one several years for the purpose of a weather-glass', is extracted from *Speculum anni, or Season on the Seasons for the Year of our Lord 1806 by Henry Season, Licensed Physician and Student in the Celestial Sciences, near Devizes.* It contains the following:

'A phial of water, containing a *leech*, I kept on the frame of my lower sash chamber window so that when I looked in the morning, I could know what would be the weather on the following day.

'If the weather proves serene and beautiful, the leech lies motionless at the bottom of the glass, and rolled together in spiral form.

'If it rains, either before or afternoon, it is found crept up to the top of its lodging and there it remains till the weather is settled.

'If we are to have wind, the poor prisoner gallops through its limpid habitation with amazing swiftness and seldom rests till it begins to blow hard.

'If a remarkable storm of thunder and rain is to succeed, for some days before, it lodges almost continually without the water, and discovers uncommon uneasiness in violent throws and convulsive-like motions.

'In the frost, as in clear summer weather, it lies constantly at the bottom; and in snow, as in rainy weather, it pitches its dwelling upon the very mouth of the phial. What reason must be assigned for them, I must leave philosophers to determine: Perhaps it may not be amiss to note, less any of the curious should try the experiment, that the leech was kept in a common eight ounce phial glass, and about three-fourths filled with water and covered on the mouth with a bit of linen rag. In the summer the water is changed once a week and in the winter once a fortnight.'

Another extract reads:

'I must acknowledge predicting the weather is a very abstruse talk, and requires a very extensive genius to perform it as it ought to be done. Sagaciously to observe the various circumstances that may alter or metamorphose the air in different parts of our island, as valleys, hills, necks of land and parts near the winding of seas and rivers, with numerous other impediments, must unavoidably render the most curious prognosticator of the weather to err oftentimes. But if an artist performs according to the rules of art, he don't deserve to be reproached or to be scandalized by every idle fellow should he sometimes miss three or four days in the weather when oftentimes it rains within twenty miles of that place the self same day ...'

The Complete Weather Guide by Joseph Taylor (1812) also refers to the leech's ability to predict the weather:

'Put a leech into a large phial three parts full of clear rain water, regularly change the same thrice a week, and let it stand on a window frame fronting the north. In fair and frosty weather it will be motionless, and rolled up in a spiral form, at the bottom of the glass; but prior to rain or snow, it will creep to the top, where, if the rain will be heavy, and of some continuance, it will remain a considerable time; if trifling, it will descend. Should the rain or snow be accompanied with wind, it will dart about its habitation with an amazing celerity, and seldom ceases until it begins to blow hard. If a storm of thunder or lightning be approaching, it will be exceedingly agitated, and express its feelings in violent convulsive starts at the top of the glass. It is remarkable, that however fine and serene the weather may be, and not the least indication of a change, either from the sky, the barometer, or any other cause whatever, yet if the animal ever shifts its position, or moves in a desultory manner, the coincident results will certainly occur within thirty-six hours; frequently within twenty-four, and sometimes in twelve; though its motions chiefly depend on the fall and duration of the wet, and the strength of the wind.'

However, should the reader think that the little leech has an easy life predicting the weather, the article on p. 211 of *Arcana of Science and Art; or an Annual Register of Popular Inventions and Improvements published by John Limbird* (London, 1830) shows that the weather can have fatal consequences for leeches. It reads:

'*Mortality among Leeches during storms*
That atmospheric changes have a remarkable influence upon leeches is a well-established fact. In 1825, M. Derheims, of St Omer, ascribed the almost sudden death of them at the approach of, or during storms, to the coagulation of the blood of these creatures, caused by the impression of the atmospheric electricity. This opinion, which at that time was the result of theory, he confirmed, in the month of March last, by direct experiment.'

Believed to have come from *Hardwick's Science Gossip* (p. 248, reference 2180) is the following advice on how to make a leech 'barometer', using an eight-ounce container containing three gills of water:

'Leech Barometer – Take an eight-ounce phial, and put in it three gills of water, and place in it a healthy leech, changing the water in summer once a week, and in winter once in a fortnight, and it will most accurately prognosticate the weather. If the weather is to be fine, the leech lies motionless at the bottom of the glass, and coiled together in a spiral form; if rain may be expected, it will creep up to the top of its lodgings and remain there till the weather is settled; if we are to have wind, it will move through its habitation with amazing swiftness, and seldom goes to rest till it begins to blow hard; if a remarkable storm of thunder and rain is to succeed, it will lodge for some days before almost continually out of the water, and discover great uneasiness in violent throes and convulsive-like motions; in frost as in clear summer-like weather it lies constantly at the bottom; and in snow as in rainy weather it pitches its dwelling in the very mouth of the phial. The top should be covered over with a piece of muslin.'

Other early books contain similar information about leech barometers, such as this extract from *Enquire Within Upon Everything*, circa 1892 (109th edition):

'802. *Leech Barometer*
Take a two ounce phial three parts filled with pure water, and place in it a healthy leech, cover the mouth of the bottle with a piece of muslin, and it will most accurately prognosticate the weather. If the weather is to be fine, the leech lies motionless at the bottom of the glass, and coiled together in a spiral form; if rain may be expected, it will creep up to the top of its lodgings, and remain there till the weather is settled; if we are to have wind, it will move through its habitation with amazing swiftness, and seldom goes to rest till it begins to blow hard; if a remarkable storm of thunder and rain is to succeed, it will lodge for some days before almost continually out of the water, and discover great uneasiness in violent throes and convulsive-like motions; in frost as in clear summer-like weather it lies constantly at the bottom, and in snow as in rainy weather it pitches its dwelling in the very mouth of the phial. The water should be changed weekly in summer and fortnightly in winter.'

In *Weather Lore* by Richard Inwards, first published in 1893, there is an illustration of a drawing he had come across in Spain, indicating the positions taken up by leeches in a 'leech barometer' (Figure 5.4). The relevant passage reads:

THE LEECH BAROMETER

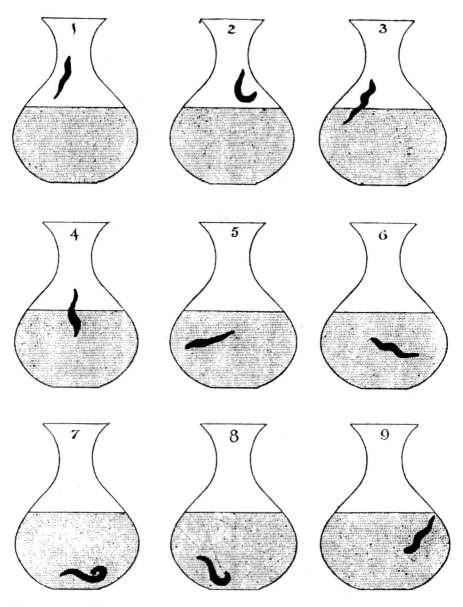

Figure 5.4: Nine positions of the leech in a Spanish drawing of a leech barometer, from Richard Inwards, Weather Lore, *1893.*

'The ordinary medicinal leech has been long regarded as a weather prophet, and I met with an old Spanish drawing in Seville, giving nine positions of the leech, with nine verses describing his behaviour under various weather conditions. On the top of the drawing was the inscription, *Dios sobre todo* (God above all). The verses were to the following effect (the numbers refer to those on the drawing):

1 If the leech take up a position in the bottle's neck, rain is at hand.
2 If he form a half-moon, when he is out of the water and sticking to the glass, sure sign of a tempest.
3 If he is in continual movement, thunder and lightning soon.
4 If he seem as if trying to raise himself from the surface of the water, a change in the weather.
5 If he move slowly close to one spot, cold weather.
6 If he move rapidly about, expect strong wind when he stops.
7 If he lie coiled up on the bottom, fine, clear weather.
8 If forming a hook, clear and cold weather.
9 If in a fixed position, very cold weather is certain to follow.'

This book also mentions Dr Merryweather's Tempest Prognosticator.

For more recent references, we can turn to *The Chemist and Druggist* of 10 November 1959, for an article by Agnes Lothian: 'Leeches commonly come up to the surface just before a thunderstorm and that the leech-gatherers find a good time to collect them. According to J. R. Johnson, "Leeches are said to predict changes in the weather with so much accuracy as to serve for barometers." Cowper asserted that leeches "in point of the earliest intelligence are worth all the barometers in the world." '

Sir Roy Sawyer, the world's authority on medicinal leeches, became interested in leeches from his early childhood and has been aware of the weather-predicting capacity of the humble medical leech for many years. In one of our many communications he states:

'From my experiences with leeches I sincerely believe there is something to leech behaviour being affected by weather. Many years ago in America I had a jar of leeches in a container for months on end. One night we had tornado warnings in the area and the leeches suddenly all crawled out of the container onto the floor. That night I went to the spot where I collected them and found the leeches well out of the water crawling some distance from the water's edge.'

I have conducted my own experiments with leeches and the weather. For a number of years we have kept leeches in a fish tank and on many occasions they have risen to the top of the tank in advance of gales and rough weather. The most interesting observations were made using leeches in the Prognosticator, which my very tolerant wife allowed me to set up in our bedroom for a number of months so we could hear the bell going off in the middle of the night.

When a leech is positioned in each of the twelve jars of the Prognosticator, with about one and a quarter inches of rainwater in the bottom, after a short time they invariably take up the same position in the jar: perhaps curled at the bottom towards the right-hand side or half in, half out of the water or towards the neck of the barometer on the left-hand side. This phenomenon was striking in that when the leeches are all in one container they naturally will have some pecking order and cannot physically take up the same place in the tank. But, individually, in the confines of their own little 'prison', they are at liberty to position themselves where they feel most comfortable.

My theory is that the leeches react weather-wise to the electrical disturbances in the air, similar to what might occur in the storm glasses described in chapter 2. Certainly, the little fellows, when disturbed, can rise up to the top and set off the mousetrap-trip affair, which rings a bell with their own individual hammer. There are, of course, one or two failings with the project, and we have come to the conclusion that leeches individually vary (just like meteorologists today) in their ability to forecast the weather. So, should you be thinking of constructing such an item as a Prognosticator, one of the instructions I would add, once built, would be to collect twelve leeches, not too old, which are good indicators of the weather. It is probable that leeches will respond more when they are active and not recently fed, so a bank of leeches would be useful in order to exchange leeches with those that are needing a rest or a feed.

One of the most common questions visitors ask when we are discussing the Prognosticator is what we feed the leeches on, and, as they are my little pets, I would not feed them on anything other than myself! Figure 5.5 shows one of them having his teaspoonful of blood.

They suck for about ten or fifteen minutes until bloated, concentrating the blood and excreting the plasma. A reasonably well-fed leech of about a year or two old can probably survive for eighteen months to two years without another feed. So in some ways they make an ideal pet!

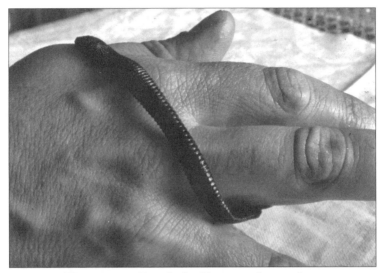

Figure 5.5: Leech feeding on the author.

Dr George Merryweather must have fed his own leeches, if they were not taken from his store of medicinal leeches for patients, and obviously became quite 'attached' to them, for he comments in his essay that, upon entering the room, his 'little comrades' came to the side of the jar where he was. I have not noticed this particular habit with any of the leeches that I have kept, but I suspect that it was more a question of movement and the hope of a feed that was enticing the leeches to move upon his entry into the room.

6　Weather Houses

A book such as this would not be complete without the inclusion of the well-known weather house. Although many people may still recognise a weather house, few will actually now own one. People's memories of them will be of a typical small, Austrian or Swiss chalet-style house, probably bought on a seaside holiday some years ago when they were children. Like so much holiday ephemera, once the children have grown up and the souvenir is dusty or broken, it is often thrown out. This makes finding old ones particularly hard and, despite my interest over a number of years, I have only managed to acquire a few at auction.

Although many people recognise the weather house, few know how it works. It is in principle a straightforward hygrometer or moisture indicator. The two figures, often a man with an umbrella and a lady with a parasol, are mounted on a horizontal board, and from the centre of this, normally unseen behind parts of the house, a small piece of cat gut rises vertically. This natural material twists left and right when it becomes dry or damp.

In *The Complete Weather Guide* of 1812 Joseph Taylor makes mention of these items: 'The Dutch toys known by the name of *weather houses* are very good hygrometers for common purposes and are formed on this principle – the contraction of the string by moisture in the atmosphere forces the male figure out of the door at the approach of *bad* weather and as it gradually becomes dry the string resumes its natural length and forces the female out of the door at the approach of *good* weather.'

It is fair to say that they are not a typically British instrument or toy, and there is little history of British weather houses. They probably originated in the mountainous regions of Switzerland in the seventeenth century, and it is likely that in these areas the high altitudes and moisture variations made it more suitable to have a weather house hung outside, especially in the days before true barometers were available. But even today they still afford a certain amount of pleasure and can give an indication of moisture: when the man comes out the air is moist and it is more likely to be raining; when the lady appears the air is dry and it is more likely to be fine. Ideally, weather houses should be positioned outside, under cover or near an airy position such as a door or window.

There is very little documented about weather houses, but I am indebted to Bert Bolle's pamphlet on weather houses (*Current Affairs*, no. 2483) for some of the information that has come to light. There are more references to weather houses in parts of Europe due to their proximity to the areas of manufacture, the German/Swiss/Austrian mountains. In his pamphlet, Bert Bolle illustrates perhaps the earliest known printed instructions believed to date from around 1700, written in Dutch. The translation reads as follows:

'Brief notes on the newly discovered weather house. How one may know daily:

'1. When the man comes out, you may expect bad weather, be it rain or wind and if in the summer he comes out in the morning, but goes back before the afternoon, one may expect that the next day there will be thunder or a strong wind. But if the man stays outside all day, you may expect rain within fifteen hours.

'2. When the heron turns sideways, where "wet" is written, he will indicate the same as the man, when he is outside. But if he turns to the side where "dry" is indicated it is the same as that which the lady indicates.

'These weather houses are sold by the "EYLENDE MAN" in the passing street.'

Different types of hygrometer have been known for a long time. As long ago as the fourteenth century observations were made using a set of scales with a ball of cotton on one scale and a counter-balance on the other. As the air became more moist or more dry, the cotton would absorb more moisture or become drier and the corresponding balance needle would indicate accordingly. It is uncertain when weather houses first appeared, although the principle of gut twisting left and right and turning a needle or dial has been known for many centuries.

This chapter, however, is interested in the common household weather house, as illustrated in Figure 6.1, which shows a fretwork wooden weather house of British manufacture from the Victorian

Figure 6.1: Victorian fretwork weather house.

Figure 6.2: Nineteenth-century European weather house.

period. Figure 6.2 is amongst the finest that I have been able to find and add to the Museum at Barometer World in Merton, and is a typical Victorian log cabin, with figures in carved wood. These are exceptionally rare and difficult to obtain. This one has suffered some damage and attack by woodworm, but is none the less a very pleasant item.

Figure 6.3 is a rather large, perhaps skilfully home-made, weather house with large carved wooden figures, dating perhaps by their dress from the Edwardian period. The inside is actually made from chocolate boxes of the period. Figure 6.4 is a continental weather house with small figures and a carved deer head between the windows. The walls are coated with glue and coloured sand. This model perhaps dates from the 1930s. It has a printed dial on the floor of the weather house (not shown), which is typical of early types of this instrument. Figure 6.5 is a simple, small weather house of European origin with wooden roof and with a thermometer, in Reaumur and centigrade scales, mounted between the small plastic figures, probably dating from the 1950s.

Figure 6.6 shows a 1960s-style weather house with many small features. Figure 6.7 is a variation which sets a real barometer within a chalet-style frame instead of using weather people. Figure 6.8 shows a 1950s' or 1960s' weather house made in Taiwan, with very simplified turned and painted figures. Figure 6.9 is a small German weather house from the 1960s with a thatched and wooden roof. There are very few British-made weather houses, but I was able to locate the weather house illustrated in Figure 6.10 which I believe to be of British origin, made of plywood with wooden figures, the paintwork somewhat worn now, probably dating from the 1950s.

Figure 6.11 is a shop display model with cast figures of a Georgian style. They were normally supplied to retailers selling Kendal umbrellas and would be displayed in the shop window. The design is quite similar to very early weather houses that occasionally come up for sale. The instructions for use are given on the reverse (Figure 6.12).

Weather houses were also made in America, and if you surf the Internet you will quite likely come across weather houses of the style illustrated in Figure 6.13. This one is from the Catskill Mountains and unpainted, made in a plastic injection mould; instead of the man and woman it has Hansel and Gretel and the Witch. This model came with its original box, illustrated in Figure 6.14, although I do not

Left, Figure 6.3: Handmade Edwardian weather house.
Right, Figure 6.4: European weather house, circa 1930s.

Left, Figure 6.5: European weather house, circa 1950s.
Right, Figure 6.6: European weather house, circa 1960s.

Left, Figure 6.7: Barometer in 'weather house', circa 1960s.
Right, Figure 6.8: Weather house made in Taiwan, circa 1950s.

Left, Figure 6.9: German weather house, circa 1960s.
Right, Figure 6.10: British weather house, circa 1950s.

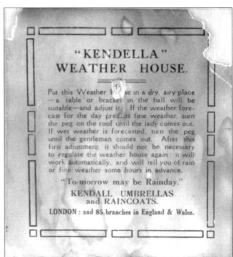

Left, Figure 6.11: Kendal umbrella company weather house, circa 1950s.

Right, Figure 6.12: Instructions on the reverse of weather house shown in Figure 6.11.

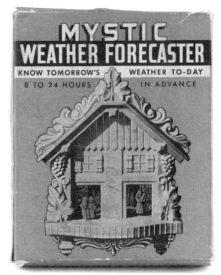

Left, Figure 6.13: American plastic weather house, circa 1960s.

Right, Figure 6.14: Original box for weather house shown in Figure 6.13.

think that the advertising on the box would pass the trading standards of today!

I am grateful to Mr Franklin who kindly took on the challenge of making weather houses for me and produced hand-built examples, as illustrated in Figure 6.15, of a Devon thatched cottage. Unfortunately, the high quality and hence price of these weather houses meant that sales were limited and today we stock the simpler, less expensive, imported varieties.

As Europe has a much greater history of involvement with weather houses, it is not surprising that we are indebted to the Dutch for a small traditional song, perhaps a nursery rhyme, about weather houses which is still remembered by Dutch people today. Bert Bolle, in his pamphlet on weather houses, had the foresight to record and write it down, but comments that there are a number of variations, as is typical with songs handed-down. Although it may have lost something in translation, it is interesting to quote it here:

'The Weather House
There's a small house hanging on the wall in the hall at Grandma's.
A pleasant gentleman and his wife go about their business.
He totes a beautiful umbrella, she carries a beautiful parasol.

If it rains, the gentleman is pleased.
He comes out for a totter around,
While the lady looks through the window.
But if the dear sun shines again,
She comes out and he disappears.

Sometimes they both stand in the doorway,
The lady and the gentleman.
Then they both view the weather with a wise expression,
And they question as to whether it will rain or the sun will shine.'

I would be interested to know if readers have any further information on weather houses or the folklore associated with them. Perhaps some readers may remember an English song, if so please do contact me. In Wales I believe they are often called Barry and Joan houses.

Over the years a number of unusual weather houses have been produced, and one that occasionally comes up in auction is the pointed

Above, Figure 6.15: Devon thatched cottage weather house of the 1990s.
Right, Figure 6.16: French tower weather house, circa 1900.
Below, Figure 6.17: Weather house St Valentine's Day telegram.

tower style, dating from around 1900, made by the establishment of Hygrona in Paris. It consists of a metal tower and a cardboard cylinder inside, which turns on catgut. This cylinder is illustrated with figures and words which become visible through the arched door and openings in the tower. It measures 10 inches high, and the base is inscribed 'Observatoire de la Tour Pointue', as illustrated in Figure 6.16.

The GPO (General Post Office) even produced a St Valentine's Day telegram in the form of a weather house (Figure 6.17), presumably to suggest that a romance could be fine weather. It is only a drawing, however, and does not move or indicate any changes in the weather.

7 Novelty Barometers

In all the preceding chapters there has been some element of weather prediction. This chapter, I freely admit, has absolutely no true weather value, but it is fitting to include some of the more comical 'barometers' that have been produced in our often quirky society.

I first started buying these novelty barometers in antique and collectors' auctions, then by on-line auction, and, as with many collections, I soon began to realise what a huge variety and large number were made. Prominent among these peculiar weather items is the 'Donkey Barometer' (Figure 7.1). So far I have not managed to track down its origins. All the ones I have come across are stamped or marked 'foreign' or German. Many have individual town names on them and were obviously meant to be sold at seaside resorts along with other souvenirs and postcards of the 'Wish you were here' variety. I suspect that their origins lie in Victorian fairings: the type of porcelain is of a cheap manufacture. Perhaps items such as this would have been brought back for Grandma or the folks back home. Often the gilded words are worn or faded and invariably the donkey's tail is missing.

The legends on the 'barometers' are often the same or have only minor variations. Figure 7.1 shows the legend printed above the donkey:

'Instructions:
If tail is dry ... Fine
If tail is wet ... Rain
If tail moves ... Windy
If tail cannot be seen ... Fog
If tail is frozen ... Cold
If tail falls out ... Earthquake'

To be accurate, the donkey barometer should be placed outside or 'put in the air'! Figure 7.2 shows three similar items in different coloured glazes. The donkey on the left, which has lost its tail, is an

Figure 7.1: Victorian donkey barometer.

almost pink lustre! The centre one is grey; while the one on the right is a blueish grey with a stand of blue lustre. The 'weather words' are all in gold-coloured lettering. The centre donkey barometer is 6.5 inches tall. Figure 7.3 shows three more donkey barometers of different sizes and designs. The one on the right is facing in a different direction from all the others I have come across. The centre one in a light grey lustre glaze measures only 4 inches tall and is the smallest one I have seen. It also has a hole to hang it or perhaps nail it outside. This donkey has no 'saddle' or girth, whereas most of the others have plain white saddles with a red/orange girth.

I was delighted when an interested visitor to the Museum, spotting our weather donkeys, recollected a story from his childhood. He managed to find the relevant book, and perhaps some of our older readers may remember *Mr Bumbletoes of Bimbleton* by L. C. Ockenden, believed to date from around the 1940s. There is a particular story called 'The Weather Donkey', about a foreign visitor selling Mr Bumbletoes what is, in fact, a weather-predicting donkey.

Curiously, the origins of the donkey and its weather-predicting tail are said to come from a donkey that lived in Peru. Its owners could tell the weather by the state of the donkey's tail: it would become limp and drooping when it was going to rain, but be stiff and dry when the weather was going to be fine. On the death of the donkey the tail was kept and eventually a part of it was used on a china donkey to foretell the weather. It would be most interesting to know whether or not there is any truth in the story. As with many curious tales, there is often some glimpse back into the past; although, as they were frequently sold as holiday souvenirs, there is also likely to be a connection with donkey rides at the seaside.

Whether Folkestone has any particular link to cats I do not know, but Figure 7.4 is an interesting variation on the theme and has a cat on a roof, entitled 'Cat Barometer'. The 'Pig Barometer' with the curly tail, shown in Figure 7.5, is another variation on this type of barometer. I wonder just how many varieties there may still be to discover.

Yet another variation on the same theme is the printed postcard. Figure 7.6 shows a mule barometer, dated 1907. These frequently turn up and I believe date originally from the Edwardian period, but have been produced in many versions ever since. Figure 7.7 shows an advertising mule barometer from New York, undated but perhaps from the 1920s. Much rarer and seldom found is the postcard shown in Figure 7.8, a 'Bully Barometer' which states that it is for ' "Pilots"

Figure 7.2: Donkey barometers, circa 1890–1920.

Figure 7.3: Donkey barometers, circa 1890–1920.

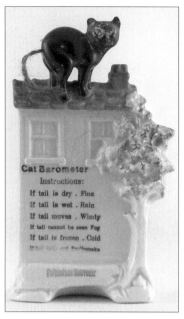

Left, Figure 7.4: Victorian cat barometer.
Right, Figure 7.5: Victorian pig barometer.

Left, Figure 7.6: Mule barometer postcard, circa 1907.
Right, Figure 7.7: Advertising barometer postcard, circa 1920.

Figure 7.8: 'Bully Barometer' postcard, circa 1907.

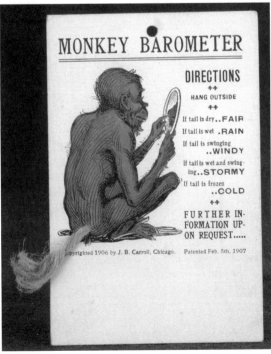

Figure 7.9: Monkey barometer postcard, circa 1907.

Figure 7.10: Camel barometer postcard, circa 1907.

Figure 7.11: A modern countryman's barometer postcard.

and Others concerned about the weather and themselves'. Figures 7.9 and 7.10 are two other variations, which are quite rare.

Not to be outdone, we produced our own postcard (Figure 7.11), but instead of using string for a tail we used good old Devonshire baler twine with which everything in Devon, when I first moved down here, seemed to be tied up, from gates and fences to van doors and even trousers!

Such weather ephemera continue to be produced, such as the modern 'weather rock' illustrated in Figure 7.12, which does not actually say it is a barometer but an accurate weather indicator complete with full explanatory leaflet. Whilst for most of us a real rock might be suitable, this one is moulded plastic! A simple modern variation is the sponge on a string 'weather detector' shown in Figure 7.13.

Cobalt Barometers

By now the intrepid collector will surely be hooked on all manner of novelty barometers, and inevitably along will come a little plaster cat, such as that illustrated in Figure 7.14, which was a present from Cheddar Gorge, whose paws are resting upon a ball of wool. Or perhaps the weather owl, which frequently appears for auction, as illustrated in Figure 7.15, and many other variations on the same theme. In Europe you will come across butterflies, and even postcard collectors may find the 'Little Weather Prophet, illustrated in Figure 7.16, which was to be hung outside, a curiosity which makes an interesting addition to a collection. The 'Parisian Perpetual Barometer' illustrated in Figure 7.17 is in exceptionally good condition, although it is not active as the chemical has long ago stopped working.

All of these 'barometers' are in fact a form of hygrometer. The ball of wool, the owl, the skirt on the postcard or some other part of a figurine or picture will change colour because of a solution of a cobalt salt covering. When dry this will be bright blue, but as it becomes moist the colour changes to pink. In 1871 Walter Bentley Woodbury of Penge, Surrey, received only provisional protection when he tried to patent this type of device in his provisional specification (see Appendix).

Figure 7.18 shows a contemporary 'Weather Cock', measuring 185 mm tall, made and sold in Portugal (the cockerel being the national emblem of Portugal). The wings and top of the tail are coated in a cobalt solution which changes colour from blue to pink in nine different

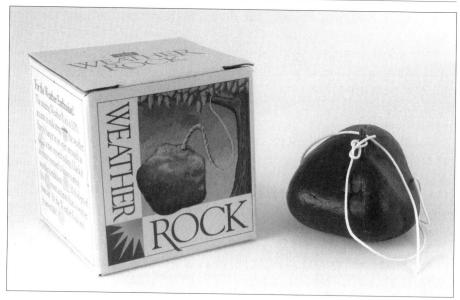

Figure 7.12: American plastic 'weather rock' barometer of the 1990s.

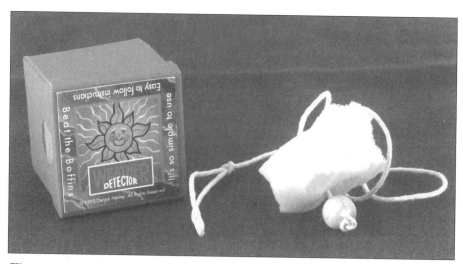

Figure 7.13: A modern 'weather sponge' barometer.

Left, Figure 7.14: Cobalt salt weather cat, circa 1960.
Right, Figure 7.15: Cobalt salt weather owl, circa 1970.

Left, Figure 7.16: Cobalt salt 'Little Weather Prophet', circa 1910.
Right, Figure 7.17: Cobalt salt Parisian perpetual barometer, circa
1895.

Figure 7.18: Modern Portuguese cobalt salt 'Weather Cock'.

shades according to the moisture in the air.

A 'barometer' theme has been used on postcards from the early days. Figure 7.19 shows 'Tommy's Love barometer' and Figure 7.20 'Jack's Love Barometer', in which, with the aid of the dial behind, the expression on our admirable serviceman's face and the appropriate words below can be changed. There are a number of other possibilities that can be dialled up, including 'She'll marry me', 'She won't', 'Let's chance it' and 'Next year'. Another jokey 'barometer' postcard is illustrated in Figure 7.21 which indicates married life in terms of the usual barometer weather words: Fair, Changeable, Rain and Storm.

Tommy's Love Barometer.

Tommy's Love Barometer.

Figure 7.19: 'Tommy's Love Barometer' postcard, circa First World War.

Jack's Love Barometer.   Jack's Love Barometer.

Figure 7.20: 'Jack's Love Barometer' postcard, circa First World War.

Figure 7.21: French 'Barometer of Married Life' postcard, circa 1910.

Appendix

Patents

Date	Number	Detail
1856	1029	Patent of various balance-type barometers, both mercury and non-mercury, utilising corrugated and evacuated tubes of various shapes by Henry Mapple.
8 April 1863	889	Improved construction of a barometer by William Haslett Mitchel.
11 April 1871	948	Colbalt salts improved barometer or hygrometer by Walter Bentley Woodbury of Penge, Surrey.
1884	16054	Cartesian type barometer by David Winstanley of Marton.
1909	26105	Improvements in and in the manufacture of instruments for foretelling changes of weather by Edward Sebastian Arrighi
12 August 1932	405,694	Means for indicating scent conditions by Hubert Maitland Budgett.

Bibliography

Adams, Thatcher, 'Letter to the Editor', *Royal Gazette*, 9 August 1970.

Arcana of Science and Art; or an Annual Register of Popular Inventions and Improvements published by John Limbird (London, 1830).

Bate, John, *The Mysteries of Nature and Art* (first edition, London, 1634).

Bolle, Bert, *Current Affairs*, no. 2483, 17 September 1993 (Leylystad, Holland: IVIO Organisation).

Cook, A. A., 'Letter to the Editor', *Weather*, vol. 21, 1966, p. 34.

Corbyn, P. R., 'A Brine Barometer', *Weather*, vol. 22, no. 9, September 1967.

Enquire Within Upon Everything (109th edition, c.1892).

FitzRoy, Robert, *The Weather Book* (second edition, London, 1863).

Fludd, Robert, *The Microcosm,* IV: 'Meteorologia Cosmica' (1626).

Grenfell, Wilfred Thomason, *The Story of a Labrador Doctor* (London: Hodder and Stoughton, [1920]).

Hardwick's Science Gossip, 18 volumes (London: Robert Hardwicke, 1865–1883).

Hayley, William, *Life of William Cowper*, vol. III (London, 1804).

Inwards, Richard, *Weather Lore* (first published 1893 by Elliot Stock of London; republished 1994 by Senate).

The Lancet, April–September, vol. 2, 1829.

Lothian, Agnes, *The Chemist and Druggist*, 10 November 1959.

Middleton, W. E. Knowles, *A History of the Thermometer and its Uses in Meteorology* (Baltimore, MD: The Johns Hopkins Press, 1966).

Ockenden, L. C., *Mr Bumbletoes of Bimbleton* (Long Acre, London: Odhams Press, c.1940).

Philosophical Transcripts, vol. 24 (Paternoster Row, London: Longman and Rees, 1803).

Rushe, George, *Your Bermuda: All You Need to Know about our Island Home* (Bermuda, G. Rushe, 1995).

Smith, Gerald, 'Shark Knows Where the Weather Is', *Sea Frontiers*, International Oceanographic Foundation, vol. 16, no. 3, May–June 1970.

Taylor, Joseph, *The Complete Weather Guide* (London, 1812).

Weather, vol. 22, no. 7, July 1967.

Index